D1062456

Warriors' Weapons

WARRIORS'

WEAPONS

Walter Buehr

Illustrated by the author

New York

THOMAS Y. CROWELL COMPANY

Established 1834

The author wishes to express his gratitude for the information contained in the following publications:

Bulletins of the Metropolitan
Museum of Art of New York

Sir Guy F. Laking,
*Record of European Arms
and Armor*

R. Ewart Oakeshott,
The Archeology of Weapons (Praeger)

Copyright © 1963 by Thomas Y. Crowell Company

Designed by Nancy H. Dale
Manufactured in the United States of America
Library of Congress Catalog Card No. 63-18412
1 2 3 4 5 6 7 8 9 10

Contents

1 The Evolution of Weapons

In this century of earth-destroying hydrogen bombs, atomic cannon, machine guns, mortars, and flame-throwers, it is hard to realize that effective firearms date back only about five hundred years. Men have always needed weapons of some kind, though, with which to kill animals and to defend themselves from other men. For more than twenty thousand years before the first crude cannon belched forth the stone projectile balanced on its muzzle, men made an extraordinary variety of ingenious, lethal, and often beautiful weapons—all of them completely independent of gunpowder.

These weapons reflected, in material and design, the constantly growing technological knowledge of man, as well as the great migrations of peoples and the clashes of civilizations.

Archeologists have found weapons from the Stone Age, which began ten to twenty thousand years before the birth of Christ and ended about 2500 B.C. Stone Age man, knowing nothing of metals, made tools and weapons of wood and stone. His earliest weapon was doubtless the club, from which eventually the spear and sword were developed. Presently he lashed a stone to the end of his club with animal sinews, to make a hammer, and when he learned how to put a sharp edge to the hammer he had an ax.

Somewhere toward the end of the Stone Age the bow and arrow appeared; how they evolved one can only guess. Still, with only his wooden clubs, stone-tipped arrows, and stone spears and axes, Stone Age man managed to kill the hairy long-tusked mastodon, the saber-toothed tiger, and other fierce prehistoric beasts.

About 2500 B.C., in Assyria, Babylonia, and Egypt, men learned to mine copper and smelt it, and later to combine it with tin to make a metal harder than either, bronze. From this new metal, smiths could hammer out keen sword blades and spear points, and even helmets, far superior to the crude weapons of the Stone Age. However, the change-over from stone to bronze was not sharp and immediate; centuries later, Norsemen from the cold northern coasts and Germans from the dark southern forests were still swinging their great, crude stone axes and hammers.

The fighting men of the Bronze Age in the lands east of the Mediterranean were foot soldiers armed with short swords and spears made of bronze. In their time they were the best soldiers in the known world. About 2000 B.C., they were conquered by the Hittites, a race of people who invaded Asia Minor, perhaps from the east, perhaps from the north; no one knows.

In time the Hittites descended upon the Egyptians, bringing a new kind of warfare resulting from their discovery and development of the wheel. Wheels and axles were first used sometime during the Bronze Age, in the form of solid wooden disks revolving on

wooden shafts. By 1800 B.C., spoked wheels, much lighter than the solid disks, were common, and carts drawn by oxen and donkeys began to carry the heavy burdens once borne on the shoulders of men or on pack animals. It was but a few steps to the swift light chariot pulled by fast horses.

Squadrons of Hittite chariots, each manned by a driver and a bowman, disorganized and decisively overwhelmed the Egyptian infantry. For a thousand years the charioteer remained supreme on the battle-field.

The Hittites also brought with them iron. Archeologists have unearthed in Egypt a wrought-iron dagger, evidently of Hittite manufacture and made before 1350 B.C. The use of iron was introduced into Greece about 1000 B.C. and later into the rest of Europe. The Celts were the first ironworkers in western Europe; they were welding bars of iron together to make long sword blades during the first century of the Christian era. These iron blades were an enormous improvement over cast-bronze blades, which couldn't be made long without being made thick and thus too heavy to wield.

In the third century B.C., the charioteer and bowman were challenged and defeated by a new form of battle tactic, originated by the Spartans, developed by the Thebans, and brought to perfection in the Macedonian phalanx of Alexander the Great. This was a sort of premotorized tank, consisting of a solid block of spearmen, sixteen rows deep, armed with the sarissa, a twenty-four-foot spear. The first row marched shoulder to shoulder, with almost overlapping shields, their spears slanting forward, while the spears of the rows behind projected from between the shields, making a thick bristling hedge of spear tips. The Macedonian phalanx plowed irresistibly through the ranks of any enemy who opposed it.

Soon, however, another force began to dominate the battlefield. This was the Roman legion, a superbly trained body of infantrymen, protected by metal helmets, breastplates, and greaves (shin guards). In the legion's battle formation of three lines of men, the first two lines were armed with the pilum, a short throwing spear about four and a half feet long, mounted on a wooden shaft of the same length and weighing four to five pounds. The third row of the legion was equipped with the hasta, a long thrusting spear. All legionaries carried in addition to the spear a two-edged sword, longer than the Greek sword, and an oval shield, four feet long, of hide-covered wood with a metal rim and boss. The pilum was made in such a way that, when it became embedded, the handle broke off to prevent re-use by the enemy. The pilum itself was pliant enough so that it bent, impeding the movements of the man it struck.

The legion soon swept the charioteer, the bowman, the spearman, and even the phalanx from the field because of its superior training, speed, and flexibility of attack. With her invincible legions, Rome occupied Gaul and Britain and dominated the entire Mediterranean basin.

Then, once again, the ever-changing pattern of war and conquest turned up new conquerors. Beginning about A.D. 200, successive waves of barbarian Teutonic tribes swept down from the north, finally overrunning the weakened Roman Empire. The barbarians' troops by A.D. 500 were cavalry, mounted on heavy, powerful horses and protected by helmets, hauberks (shirts of mail), and long shields. They were armed with long iron-tipped lances, axes, and maces as well as long, straight, cut-and-thrust swords, quite different from the short stabbing swords of the legions.

The Romans held back the horsemen from the north for a time; but in A.D. 378, at the Battle of Adrianople, in Turkey, the Goths completely routed

6

the Roman infantry, killing 40,000, including the emperor and almost all high officers. This battle decisively broke the Roman legion's power.

How was the Gothic cavalry able to defeat the seasoned Roman infantry so thoroughly? Cavalry had been used in battle for many hundreds of years; it had always before been defeated by the legions. The difference lay in the superb horsemanship of the Goths and in a simple invention, unknown to the ancients, which permitted a cavalryman to wield a long lance or broadsword with one hand, hold his shield and reins in the other, and still remain securely in the saddle. This was the stirrup.

The stirrup is believed to have originated in Assyria about 850 B.C., and there is proof that it also existed in China during the Han dynasty, roughly from 200 B.C. to A.D. 200. It first appeared in Europe about A.D. 441 during the invasion by the Huns, those wild horsemen from the steppes who overran Europe under Attila.

Centuries of strife followed the fall of Rome. During those anarchic times, when there were kings but no central governments, strong leaders built castles and gathered around them bands of armed knights. These men swore fealty to their lord, as he did to his lord, who in turn pledged allegiance to the king. It was the duty of knights to defend their lord, his castle, and his retainers and peasants against attack. In return he gave them the shelter of his castle and supplied them with arms and food—and later with land. This was the essence of feudalism.

Between the tenth and fifteenth centuries the feudal castle developed from a simple tower surrounded by wooden palisades and a ditch to the massive, battlemented stone fortress with double or triple curtain walls and a deep, water-filled moat. The seemingly impregnable castle fortress challenged the inventive genius of the medieval engineer. He soon came up with a number of siege machines: missile-throwing catapults, siege towers, battering-rams. These weapons all operated, of course, without benefit of explosives.

Meanwhile, battlefield techniques were based on the Gothic cavalry. Feudal knights were armed like the Goths, but until the middle of the eleventh century arms and armor were very heavy and clumsy indeed. The sheer weight and brute strength of a shoulder-to-shoulder charge swept over the enemy. Only occasionally did armored knights engage in single combat on the field of battle. From the sixth to the eleventh centuries military arms, armor, and tactics changed very little. It needed the Crusades to bring about a change.

In 1096, Pope Urban II proclaimed a holy crusade against the Moslem infidels occupying the Holy Land. The kings of England, France, and the Holy Roman Empire called upon their barons to enlist knights and retainers for a march on the Holy City.

Most of Europe's feudal knights embarked on one

or another of the eight crusades that were launched between 1096 and 1291. In clashes with the Saracen warriors they soon discovered that the followers of Mohammed had chain mail lighter and stronger than their own, steel swords far superior to their clumsy

blades, and mounted archers deadlier than their own bowmen.

During the almost two hundred years that the Crusaders invaded the Holy Land, the knights adopted the best features of their opponents' arms and armor, developed new weapons of their own, such as the crossbow, and learned how to counter Moslem tactics.

When the Crusaders returned to their homes in Europe, feudal armorers and swordsmiths used what they had learned in the Holy Land to forge better weapons and armor; with these the mounted knight became the unchallenged master of the battlefield. A charge of these mighty men-at-arms, mounted on their massive, snorting destriers, always scattered enemy archers and spearmen; the only soldiers who could hope to stand up to them were other mounted knights. Yet in less than a hundred years an English adaptation of a Welsh weapon was to spell the doom of the mounted knight and make him as obsolete as the chariot.

This weapon was the longbow. The bow had long been used in warfare, but the early longbow was not strong enough to penetrate armor. The crossbow, which came later, was much more effective, but it took so long to pull back the bowstring with ratchet or lever that enemy horsemen could run down a line of bowmen before they got off more than two or three bolts.

The English longbow was a powerful six-foot

weapon. Its deadly efficiency in the hands of his Welsh allies during the Scottish wars so impressed Edward III of England that he insisted upon every English villager's practicing with the longbow until he could shoot with accuracy and speed. In battle a company of English archers could keep hundreds of arrows flying through the air at one time; some were bound to wound enemy knights at weak points in their armor, or at least put many horses out of action —and without his horse a knight was almost helpless.

The Battle of Crécy, between the English and French armies in 1346, proved conclusively the superiority of the English longbow. At Crécy the English battle line consisted of dismounted knights in close order, presenting a line of lances, flanked by two wings of longbowmen. These archers slaughtered the French crossbowmen who attacked first, then brought low the horses of the French knights, leaving them helpless against the charge of the reserves of English knights.

It seemed then that English knights and infantry together were unparalleled in war, but at the same time the Swiss were winning battles with infantry alone. Deploying masses of men carrying eighteen-foot pikes, they developed an improvement on Alexander's ancient phalanx. When a man in the first row fell he was at once replaced by the man behind him, thus keeping a solid thicket of points against which enemy cavalry charges broke, unable to penetrate. For a time the new Swiss formation was so successful that other armies hired Swiss mercenaries to help them win their battles.

In the sixteenth century the Swiss phalanx was itself defeated by the new methods of the spirited Spanish infantry, the finest foot soldiers of the time. The agile, lightly armored Spaniards, equipped only with cuirasses, steel caps, small shields, and their

swords, simply advanced on the phalanx, forced the Swiss to open their ranks, and in close combat, in which the long pike was useless, skewered the helpless foe.

Eventually gunpowder took command of the battlefield. In the fourteenth century the cannon and the harquebus, or hand gun, were improved until they began to be really formidable in battle. Even then the archer fought alongside the musketeer, whose gun took a long time to load. For more than two hundred years armies usually contained companies of both.

Weapons of the Stone Age

2

The Stone Age—the era before man learned to use metals—has been roughly divided by archeologists into three periods. The Old Stone Age, or Paleolithic period, began when our earliest ancestors learned to use sticks and stones to defend themselves and to bring down game. They flaked and sharpened pieces of stone for tools and weapons at least 600,000 years ago. The Middle Stone Age, or Mesolithic period (about 10,000 B.C. to 5000 B.C.), and the New Stone Age, or Neolithic period (about 5000 B.C. to 3000 or 2000 B.C.), are defined by marked advances in technology. The Neolithic period merges with the era when men began to mine copper and make tools and weapons of metal.

Early Stone Age man probably used large stones naturally shaped for his purposes, or sharp chips broken off larger stones by nature. Peking man improved these natural implements by chipping or hammering them with other stones. Early prehistoric man in Africa made tools of pebbles, one edge of which he flaked to sharpness. A later culture in Tanganyika made unhafted axes by flaking both edges of a stone slab into a tongue-shaped tool or weapon.

Paleolithic man constantly improved his methods of flaking and hence his tools. He manufactured two main types: core tools and flake tools. He turned a stone into a core tool by trimming and chipping it. To make a flake tool he struck a large stone in such a way that it broke into smaller pieces, and from these pieces, or flakes, he then fashioned tools. Core tools were made mostly by Stone Age men in Africa and Asia; flake tools were made in western Asia and Europe. Paleolithic man used almost any kind of stone which was handy and easy to work. Obsidian, the hard glasslike rock left by volcanic eruptions, and flint were especially desirable because they could be chipped easily and retained a razor-sharp edge. Ledges of flint were not always on the surface, however; prehistoric man had to turn miner to reach flint buried under eight or ten feet of earth. At first he dug wide, open trenches to the flint and chopped it out in chunks. Later he dug shafts and tunnels in search of the precious stone.

Certainly early Stone Age men used some materi-

17

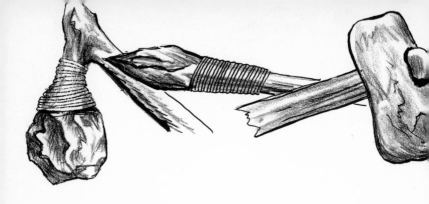

als other than stone: bone, ivory, horn, and, most important, wood. Few of these were able to survive over long periods of time, however; hence we do not know how widely they were worked. Clearly it was natural for a man to shape a broken tree branch into a club to wield against an enemy—man or beast—or to sharpen a stick to use as a spear, fork, or poker. Often the very shapes of stone spearheads and ax-heads indicate that the weapons once had wooden attachments. Of the few prehistoric wooden implements that have been found intact, one of the most important is a pointed spear discovered with stone implements in a peat deposit in Essex, England. Made of yew, the spear gives evidence of having been shaped by sharp flint flakes, perhaps like one of the stone scrapers found with it.

Middle Stone Age artisans learned to lash wooden handles to their stone weapons with strips of raw-hide, animal sinews, or tough grasses or vines. Illus-

18

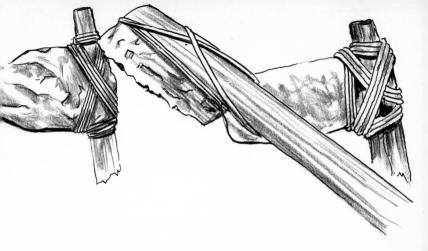

trated are axes, hammers, spearheads, and knives as they probably looked when their owners were alive.

A wooden handle lashed to a stone head was not very secure; eventually a clever Stone Age man devised a way to drive a hole through a stone. If he heated the flint in a fire and then poured drops of cold water on one spot, repeating the action again and again, at last the stone would crack and crumble a bit. After a while he could make a hole, through which he hammered a handle. This made a stronger tool than one with a lashed-on haft.

Reversing this idea, the Aztecs made formidable swords by inserting long, sharp-edged slivers of obsidian into slots cut lengthwise in a wooden club.

Late Stone Age man learned how to make bows and arrows and thereby invented a better way of making holes in stone. He wrapped a bowstring several times around the shaft of an arrow then restrung the bow. Holding the arrow upright with its stone head pressed against the object to be pierced, he moved the bow rapidly back and forth, making the arrowhead revolve even more rapidly; this was the first drill.

When the last Glacial Age brought ice and cold, Stone Age man retired to caves, which he partially blocked with stones, tree limbs, and skins. When he sallied forth to hunt, he wore fur garments sewed with needles carved from bones and held together with bone buttons.

Finally he learned to domesticate animals, first the dog, then the pig, and finally all the domestic animals we know today, except the cat and the chicken. He cultivated grain, built huts, made pottery, and learned to grind and polish his stone tools and weapons. Further development had to await the discovery of copper and tin and methods of smelting and combining them.

Weapons of the Bronze Age

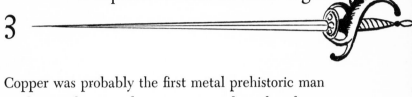

3

Copper was probably the first metal prehistoric man used to make utensils, weapons, and works of art. (Many archeologists believe gold was first.) Copper seems to have appeared in many places throughout antiquity, though not simultaneously. The Sumerians of Mesopotamia used it as early as 3500 B.C. The Assyrians, Babylonians, and Egyptians were working it into bronze by 2500 B.C., with ore brought from Asia Minor. The ancient Chinese and Japanese also knew and used copper.

Copper was discovered in England as early as 2000 B.C., and was also worked somewhat later in Germany, France, Spain, Portugal, Russia, and especially in the Austrian Tyrol in large quantities. Huge mounds of slag from copper-smelting furnaces dating from 1600 B.C. have been found in Crete. When the Greeks fought against the Trojans in the series of wars between 1200 and 1100 B.C., troops on both sides of the war were armed with bronze weapons.

At first, copper was picked up as particles and

nuggets, but native copper was soon exhausted, and miners began to dig out ore from veins at or near the surface, a practice which continued for centuries.

Early Tyrolean copper miners, for example, dug shafts down which they climbed on notched tree trunks to the galleries below. There, using torches for light, they set fires to split the rock, then took up bronze or stone hammers to knock out chunks of ore. After carrying the ore back up the ladders in sacks slung across their shoulders, they pounded it into small particles before melting it down. Later, ore was hauled up in baskets by windlasses. These men knew how to shore up the sides of their shafts with timbers to prevent cave-ins, and they may have built fires at the bottoms of the shafts to make the foul air rise. However, until Thomas Newcomen invented the steam engine in the eighteenth century, which made possible the pumping and ventilating of mine shafts by mechanical means, mining had reached its greatest extent. When a mine grew so deep that flooding and bad air got out of control, it was simply abandoned.

Early copper workers found that copper was easy to recover even in crude, low-temperature furnaces, soft to work, and impervious to rust. Its durability and the fact that it could be molded and hammered into a variety of shapes were its chief advantages over stone as a raw material for weapons. Its softness was actually a disadvantage, since that meant it could not hold a sharp edge. In a relatively short time, early metalworkers began to form harder alloys of copper with other metals, such as gold and antimony. Copper's most successful alloy was tin. There were prehistoric tin mines in Spain, Brittany, and Germany, but the largest by far were in Cornwall, England. In those early days ships from all over the known world filled their holds with tin from the Cornish mines.

Bronze was stronger and harder, and thus more useful than copper. A mild bronze was made with 5 per cent tin added to the copper, while a 15 per cent proportion resulted in a hard bronze capable of retaining a sharp edge. Molten bronze was run into molds to make cast-bronze articles. Flat objects were made by pouring the bronze into stone or sand molds in which the design had been chipped or scooped. Larger rounded objects were made in molds of two or more sections. Bronze can fill even the tiniest and most delicate parts of a mold completely, so that it was used in statues, complicated decorative objects, and of course the blades of weapons.

Unlike iron (see next chapter), copper and bronze grow softer when they are heated and cooled quickly.

They can be hardened only when hammered in the cold state. Prehistoric smiths toughened the edges of bronze weapons by repeated hammering.

The discovery and working of bronze made possible weapons far superior to the chipped flint axes and spears of Stone Age man. The first bronze weapons were the unhafted ax and knife, shaped much like those of the Stone Age and useful both domestically and for war. Soon these were cast with sockets, and then it was simple enough to fasten the knife to the end of a long pole to make a spear, and the axhead to a shorter piece of wood to make a battle-ax.

Gradually Bronze Age knife blades grew longer and narrower until a new weapon was created—the sword. The earliest swords were all thrusting weapons, or rapiers, with slender almost symmetrical blades. The handles of early Celtic swords were usually fastened to the blades with rivets, which held well enough when a straight thrust was made but tended to pull out sideways when a lateral or hacking strain was put on the blade. Later on, sword and hilt were cast all in one piece to solve this problem. Then the hilt consisted of a flat narrow tongue (called the tang), to the sides of which plates of wood or bone were attached, again by rivets. Or, sometimes, a tapered tang was inserted into a wooden handle.

CASTING BRONZE WEAPONS AND TOOLS

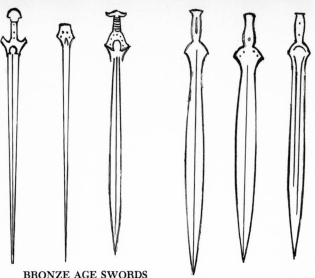

BRONZE AGE SWORDS

Either arrangement resulted in a hilt sturdy enough to withstand the strain of hacking. Still it required a great deal of experience to cast a blade with a narrow yet strong tang; bronze was brittle and broke easily.

Middle Bronze Age swords had leaf-shaped blades, a style also adopted by the Greeks and Romans. This shape was unexcelled for cut-and-thrust, close hand-to-hand fighting. The long sharp points were very effective for stabbing; the heavier curved part of the blade just behind the point was just right for a cutting stroke, while the reverse curve up near the hilt lent itself ideally to a backhand stroke.

Later on, swords were made with wider, heavier blades in several shapes. The Hallstat, the carp's-tongue, and the Rhone Valley types are illustrated

26

here. It is generally agreed among students of arms that early Bronze Age swords were used only for thrusting, the middle period blades for both cutting and thrusting, and the later ones for cutting only. The early blades had their greatest weight toward the tip, for the most effective balance in stabbing or thrusting. Later blades were cast with the greatest weight farther back, for better balance in cutting. The later swords had a greater proportion of tin to copper to make the metal harder and better able to hold an edge.

The hilts of most Bronze Age swords were so short that one might conclude the warriors of that time had extremely short, small hands. However, these short hilts were designed to have only three fingers wrapped around them—the middle, fourth, and pinky fingers. The forefinger was held straight forward, with its tip resting on the shoulder or flat part of the blade, just below the hilt, and the thumb gripped the other side firmly. This grip facilitated aim and control of the blade.

While the sword was the principal weapon of the Bronze Age, bronze-tipped spears were also much used, and warriors wore helmets of bronze and carried shields with bronze faces (backed by layers of hide for strength).

CARP'S-
TONGUE
SWORD

27

RHONE VALLEY SWORD

Weapons of the Iron Age

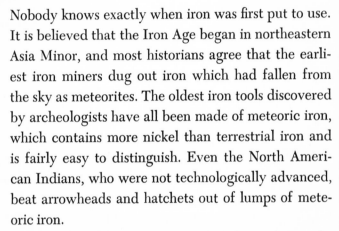

4

Nobody knows exactly when iron was first put to use. It is believed that the Iron Age began in northeastern Asia Minor, and most historians agree that the earliest iron miners dug out iron which had fallen from the sky as meteorites. The oldest iron tools discovered by archeologists have all been made of meteoric iron, which contains more nickel than terrestrial iron and is fairly easy to distinguish. Even the North American Indians, who were not technologically advanced, beat arrowheads and hatchets out of lumps of meteoric iron.

By about 1400 B.C., men were applying the smelting process, previously used for other metals, to separate iron from iron ore. They knew from their experience with copper that wood fires were not hot enough for a reducing furnace but that fires of charcoal—obtained by charring wood in airtight ovens—were. They had learned, too, that a draft of air directed over the flames caused the fire to burn more fiercely and raised the temperature. Some of the first iron-smelting furnaces, like many early copper-smelting furnaces, were sunk into the side of a hill to take advantage of the updraft of the wind; but the L-shaped copper furnace was modified to a dome shape in order to hold more iron ore and fuel. Later, bellows came into use and free-standing shaft furnaces were built.

A typical iron-smelting furnace of later Roman times was made up of alternate layers of charcoal and iron ore in a beehive shape. The pile was covered by a thick layer of clay with three holes: one at the top to act as a chimney; one at the side, near the bottom, into which a bellows was inserted; and the third in the opposite side to allow slag to run off.

Unlike copper or the other metals of antiquity, iron could not simply be smelted—melted in the furnaces to a flowing liquid—and then used; for the result was a spongy "bloom," composed of softened pieces of metal mixed with gangue—the slag and cinders. (Early experimenters with iron ore, so accustomed to a liquid product, probably did not even notice the metal globules mingled with the gangue; this may have delayed the Iron Age even after many peoples recognized veins of ore in the earth.) The early ironsmiths had to pound the bloom a long time, usually reheating it and rehammering it, in order to beat out the slag and other impurities it contained.

The end product of this smelting process was wrought iron. But wrought iron is too soft to hold a sharp edge. Bronze remained the metal of choice for weapons. The big advance in technology came with the invention of steel, which followed almost immediately after the discovery of iron. Steel is harder and tougher than iron or bronze. The first steelmakers possessed a "secret weapon" as overwhelmingly powerful in the second millennium B.C. as the atomic bomb was in the twentieth century.

The difference between iron and steel lies in the amount of carbon mixed with the metal. The quantity of carbon involved is astonishingly small. A fraction of a per cent one way or the other causes radical changes in the properties of the product. The soft wrought iron that the first smiths obtained from ore contained practically no carbon at all—although the ore was smelted in contact with charcoal, most of the carbon reacted with elements (chiefly oxygen) in the ore; the rest of the carbon was beaten out by hammering. Steel must contain between about .15 and 1.5 per cent carbon. (Still more carbon—1.5 to 5 per cent—characterizes cast iron, but this material was not known to the ancients.)

Soon after 1400 B.C., the Hittites learned how to

convert wrought iron into steel by carburization (also called cementation). Some experts date the true beginning of the Iron Age to the origin of this process. Iron was heated for hours in contact with charcoal, then hammered, then reheated, and rehammered repeatedly until the carbon in the charcoal united with the iron to change its outer surfaces to steel. (It is difficult if not impossible to turn the whole of a piece of iron into steel unless the iron is melted to a liquid, and this could not be done until the blast furnace was invented during the Middle Ages.)

The following centuries brought two other developments that made steel weapons almost as good as they can be made today. The first of these was quenching—reheating steel to a high temperature and cooling it abruptly by plunging it into cold water. This made the metal very hard but brittle. Later the degree of hardness was controlled by the second process: tempering. The steel was heated again after quenching, but this time cooled gradually. The result was a very hard, very tough steel that could be ground to give a very sharp and long-lasting edge.

From 1200 B.C. on, the Egyptians and other iron-makers knew carburization only. Between 900 and 700 B.C., ironmasters used quenching. By Roman times, steel was being tempered.

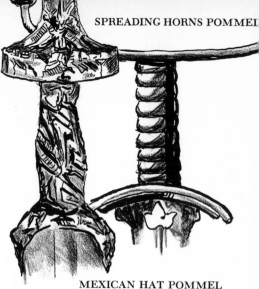

MUSHROOM POMMEL

MEXICAN HAT POMMEL

Steel was made by these methods until comparatively recent times, when the Bessemer and open-hearth furnaces were invented.

Iron was—and still is—abundant at the surface, so that it was usually not necessary to dig deep mines in order to extract it. What iron mines there were, were similar to the early copper mines. During the Middle Ages, men found beds of iron ore in ponds and bogs, where, working from boats, they extracted it with tongs. In winter they pulled it up through holes in the ice.

First mined extensively in northeastern Asia Minor, iron was also exploited in Spain, Gaul, Britain, and

CHAPE

Austria and southern Germany well before Roman times. The people of the Hallstat region in Austria were smelting copper and iron ores and forging bronze and iron weapons between 1000 and 950 B.C.

Hallstat is part of a salt-mining area in upper Austria. While not the site of the beginning of the Iron Age, it was a rich source of iron ore and could be called the cradle of early European ironmaking. In its ancient graves, archeologists found some of the earliest iron objects, dating from 1000 to 800 B.C., and could trace the transition from bronze to iron in early weapons.

The long, heavy iron swords of the Hallstat iron-workers were clearly of the slashing variety, since their points were not sharp but almost squared off at the tips. The hilts had pommels, or knobs, at the ends. These were of three distinctive styles, named for their shapes: the mushroom, the Mexican hat, and the spreading horns.

GREEK KOPIS

During the five hundred years before the beginning of the Christian era when Roman arms ruled the Mediterranean basin, barbarians to the north and west were already forging the kinds of weapons which would conquer Rome centuries later. The great iron double-edged swords made by these Teutonic peoples were about thirty-six inches long, with blades as much as two and a half inches wide at the six-inch hilt, and tapering to nearly two inches at the tip.

Some of the scabbards for these long swords had chapes (fittings at the lower end) extending in wings as much as seven inches on each side. They were there for a purpose; when a mounted warrior, his left hand busy gripping his shield and reins, wanted to draw his sword with his right, he could hook one wing of the chape behind his left leg and hold the

ROMAN LEGIONARIES AND LEGION SWORD

scabbard in place. During this period the scabbards of swords forged in continental Europe were of wood covered with leather, while many of those found in Britain were of bronze.

The swords of the barbarian warriors of the north were longer than Roman blades for a good reason. The invaders did much of their fighting from chariots, and a charioteer needed a long blade to reach his adversaries. Some chariots had two wheels of solid wood; others had four. The charioteers, instead of dashing headlong into the enemy's ranks, galloped as close as possible to, and parallel with the foe's front line, uttering terrifying yells and hurling javelins and arrows into his ranks, in the hope of causing confusion and panic as their own infantry charged.

Besides the sword, these northern barbarians wielded the spear, the war ax, the hammer, and the

BARBARIANS WITH
LONG IRON SWORD

flail, and presently a quite different type of sword called the sax. This was a single-edged weapon with a broad, slightly curved blade, a more sharply curving edge, and an acute point. The ancestor of the sax was the Greek kopis; its medieval descendant, in a slightly different form, was the falchion; its modern offspring is the cavalry saber. Perhaps because of its shape, it made a good cleaver or hacking weapon. At any rate, it remained in use for centuries in one form or another. Old manuscripts mention that many warriors preferred the sax to the long sword, and modern-day cavalry evidently found the saber a handier weapon than the straight broadsword.

For the history of weapons from the first to the seventh centuries, historians are greatly indebted to the northern pagans, who buried vast quantities of arms and armor along with the bodies of their great war lords. In the 1850's and '60's, archeologists began to dig out of Danish peat bogs unbelievably rich deposits of arms, armor, jewelry, household utensils, and even clothing, as well as skulls and bones of men and horses.

These artifacts had evidently been placed there between A.D. 50 and 450, when the bogs were small lakes or ponds, as part of a burial custom observed all through the Norse country. They owed their fine state of preservation to the forming around them of peat, its chemical properties having preserved wood and, in some cases, fabric from rotting for more than eighteen hundred years.

In one bog at Nydam, four ships, two small ones and two larger ones in fair condition, were uncovered. In a bog at Thorsbjerg, south of Flensberg in South Jutland, Denmark, an enormous number of items were found. There were many swords, both single and double edged, bows, arrows, spears, sword belts and buckles. Some of the decorative objects and jewelry had been inlaid with gold and silver and ornamented with precious stones. Roman coins and cavalry swords were discovered, as well as shields made of boards faced with bronze. Here, too, archeologists found pattern-welded sword blades that led to the rediscovery of this ancient metallurgical technique (see Chapter 5).

When the pagans migrated to southern Europe and were Christianized, they abandoned the practice of burying artifacts in lakes or graves, so that specimens of early weapons are more plentiful than those dating from later centuries. Besides the weapons found in those burial cairns, many have turned up from time to time in the mud of river beds and in excavations on the sites of great battles. The individual tombs of great lords are another rich source.

After the breakup of the Roman Empire at the end of the fifth century, the heavily armored cavalryman, mounted on a powerful war horse and armed with lance, battle-ax, flail, and long sword, ruled the battlefield for a thousand years. He was to remain the deciding factor in battle almost until the advent of the firearm, disputed only for a few short years by the English longbow. This mounted warrior, descendant of the Teutonic fighters of the north, was the forefather of the feudal knight.

The history of weapons from the fall of Rome to the advent of gunpowder is chiefly the history of feudal weapons. The greatest development in arms and armor took place between the tenth and fifteenth centuries and reached its peak during the late thirteenth and early fourteenth centuries. From the simple sword and spear, armorers progressed to weapons with such strange-sounding names as halberds, catchpoles, and guisarmes, while the crossbow and longbow grew steadily more destructive. Then, as the world entered the Age of Firearms, the edged and pointed weapon was gradually used less and less in battle and more and more as a ceremonial symbol, until today, except for the bayonet and the commando knife, cold steel is no longer a material of war.

The Sword

5

The lord of battles, aristocrat of weapons, the sword was usually carried only by men of noble blood. Legend mentions many famous swords with magic properties, such as Excalibur, the famous blade which King Arthur took at the direction of the Lady of the Lake from the hand rising out of the waters.

The mystique attached to swords is seen in the Norse saga of Hrolf Kraki. He was an Icelandic chieftain whose great sword Skofnung was buried with him along with his armor and other weapons, as was the custom among the Norse war chiefs. Hrolf Kraki's weapons were most carefully wrapped in wax-impregnated cloth to preserve them, so that some worthy descendant might years later dig them up and use them himself. Legend had it that only a properly identified warrior could penetrate the magic protecting Skofnung and gain use of the blade.

Some two hundred years after Hrolf Kraki's death, a formidable Icelandic warrior named Skeggi braved the magic spell and dug up the sword. Skeggi must have understood Skofnung's magic, because the sword served him well and faithfully all his life, and afterward his son as well.

While Skeggi still owned the great sword, a head-strong young warrior named Kormac challenged a quarrelsome ruffian named Bersi, who possessed a powerful sword. Kormac knew he would have no chance without an equally potent blade. At his mother's urging he called upon Skeggi to beg for the loan of Skofnung. Skeggi hesitated but finally agreed with many reservations. Kormac was never to remove the bag covering the hilt of the sword, for the sun must not be permitted to shine upon the hilt, and he was never to draw the sword from its scabbard in the presence of a woman, or until it was to be wielded in combat. What was more, Kormac was to blow upon the blade when he drew it; a small snake would then wriggle out from under the hilt, and must be respect-fully allowed to return to the hilt. Skeggi also showed Kormac a mysterious bead dangling from the hilt. This, he said, was the Life Stone. No wound caused by Skofnung's blade would ever heal until it was rubbed by the Life Stone. Archeologists have found similar beads—of pottery, glass, meerschaum, and stone—buried beside Norse swords. Kormac returned home and in his rashness disregarded Skeggi's warning. He tried to show Skofnung to his mother, but the sword howled and refused to leave its scabbard. Later, at the dueling ground, he removed the bag from the hilt, heedlessly exposing the hilt to the sun. When he tried to unsheathe the blade it refused to be withdrawn until he put his foot on the guard. Then it came out with a howl. But now its luck had changed and it would not defend Kormac. He was killed in the duel.

In feudal days the sword was still greatly respected. The climax of the ceremony conferring knighthood on a young squire came when his sponsor smote him on each shoulder with his own sword, saying, "I dub thee knight." On the rare occasions when a man's knighthood was taken from him, for breaking some tenet of the code, he was brought before a conclave of his peers, to whom the charges were read out. If he was found guilty the ceremony of degradation was invoked: a jar of water was dashed in his face, his spurs were removed, and his sword was broken before him. This ceremony was carried into modern times and is still observed in some armies. An officer to be cashiered is summoned before assembled

DEGRADATION OF A KNIGHT

troops; the buttons of his tunic are ripped off and his sword is broken.

When soldiers in the field capitulated, their commander offered his sword, hilt first, to the winning commander in token of unconditional surrender. The victorious commander, realizing that his opponent's honor went with the sword, was usually true to the code of the military caste and returned it.

At times during the sword's long history, attempts were made to regulate its size as well as its use. In the reign of Bloody Mary in England (from 1553 to 1558), the maximum length of a rapier was restricted to forty and a half inches. This was reduced during the reign of Elizabeth I to thirty-six inches.

In 1628, Spanish ordinance dictated that sword or rapier blades must not exceed one and a quarter yards in length, and forbade anyone to carry a dagger unless he also wore a sword. Furthermore, nobody could carry arms of any kind after ten o'clock at night, unless he also carried a lighted lantern or a torch.

The sword played an important part in the swearing of oaths, the dubbing of knights, the swearing of allegiance. During the swearing of an oath of allegiance, the liege lord placed his hand on top of his sword, at the point where the blade joined the hilt, while the vassal put his hand underneath, at the same time kissing the lord's hand. Some swords had small rings hanging from the pommel, which the vassal

SPANISH LAW OF 1628

kissed during a swearing; such a ceremony was called a "ring oath."

Swords have survived into the present day as ceremonial symbols, especially at the court of kings, and as presentation weapons, marks of honor given to distinguished men. In the armed forces, they were long worn by officers as both a weapon and a mark of rank, but now they are worn only on ceremonial occasions. Until the invention of the rapid-fire gun, the saber and the lance were as important to the cavalryman as the carbine; today the cavalry charge and the cavalryman himself have disappeared.

How were swords made? Since early iron-smelting furnaces were not hot enough to melt iron completely, the early smith had to work with chunks of fairly solid metal. With the chunks he culled from the smelted "bloom," he hammered out a flat piece of iron and carburized it. This piece of iron would serve as a sword blade, but it was "steeled" only on its outer edges, soft at the core. In order to make stronger blades with a more heterogeneous carbon—hence steel—content, the swordsmith developed a more complicated process. He hammered out a number of flat slender bars of carburized iron. Then he packed them together, reheated the bundle, and forge-welded them into one piece of metal.

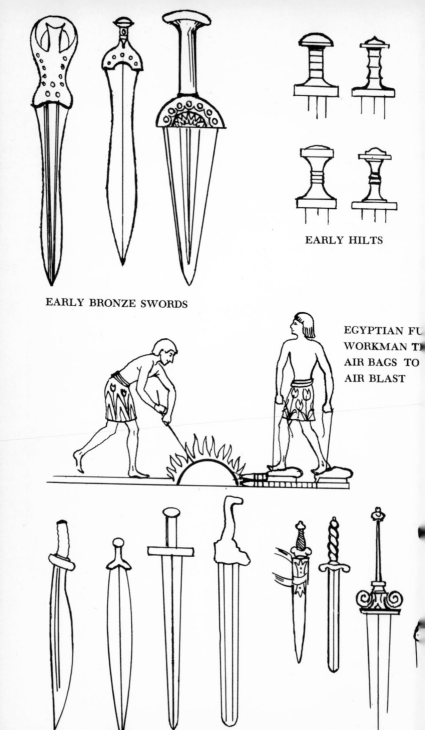

EARLY BRONZE SWORDS

EARLY HILTS

EGYPTIAN FU
WORKMAN T
AIR BAGS TO
AIR BLAST

GREEK BLADES

IRON SWORDS

TO FOURTEENTH CENTURY   FOURTEENTH TO SIXTEENTH CENTURY

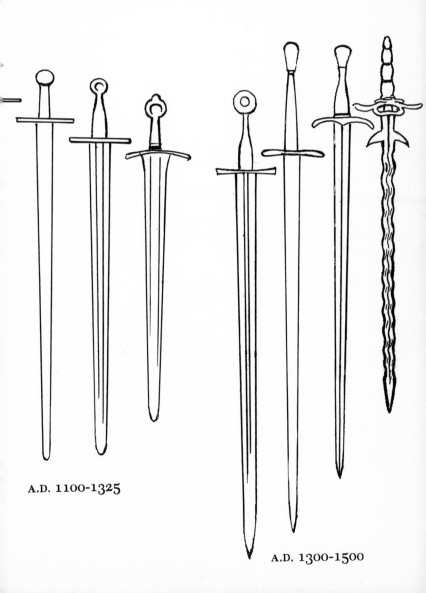

A.D. 1100-1325

A.D. 1300-1500

Going one step further the Roman swordmaker twisted the bars that were to be forged, heated them, then hammered them into a piece of metal, which was to become the core of a sword blade. On each side of this core he placed a flat bar of carburized iron, then heated the three sections together, and finally hammered and filed them into one smooth blade.

The finished blade showed faintly the pattern of the twisted bars of the center section, a beautiful snakelike design. This process was called pattern welding, and it was practiced by the Romans during the second century, later by the Vikings, and by European swordsmiths up until about A.D. 1000. The so-called Damascus sword, made in Syria, India, and Persia from the first century on by a somewhat different process (although damascening is often used inaccurately as a synonym for pattern welding), achieved great renown after the tenth century.

Examination of the twisted design in the pattern-welded blade accounts for the legend of the snake that emerged from the hilt of Skofnung. When warm breath is blown against a pattern-welded blade, the dim, twisted, snakelike pattern suddenly emerges clear and distinct upon the metal.

These blades were sometimes polished or etched with chemicals to make the design stand out on the surface. The pattern, which shows the strength and toughness of the blade, is caused by irregular crystallization due to the slow cooling of high-carbon crucible steel repeatedly heated and forged to form the blade.

Ancient swordsmiths of the East sometimes sprinkled white-hot blades with diamond and ruby dust, which was beaten into the metal with a mallet. The carbon from the diamond dust and the aluminum from the ruby dust turned the iron into hardened steel. Old-time Turkish swordsmiths used for their finest blades only iron obtained from melting down

long-used horseshoes, because they believed that the horses' hoofs somehow refined the iron in the shoes. Odd as it may sound, this belief proved to have a solid scientific basis; modern steelmakers always use a proportion of old scrap metal in making steel.

After about A.D. 900, archeologists have found, sword blades were made stronger and thinner and all in one piece of solid steel by the improved crucible method. The iron and charcoal were placed in a fire-clay crucible and heated to a much higher temperature before forging.

The earliest swords had hilts which were simply rounded extensions of the blades, without guards or pommels. Presently, as we have seen, the hilts were riveted to the upper ends of the blades; and finally, especially after the discovery of iron, the blade was forged with one end narrowing into a tongue, called a tang, which became the core of the hilt.

The grip, that part of the hilt grasped by the hand, was either slotted and driven onto the tang, or made in two pieces, sandwiched around the tang, and secured by rivets. Throughout history swordsmiths, jewelers, and engravers have lavished their skills upon sword hilts. They used gold, silver, copper, and iron as well as precious stones, jade, and ivory to garnish or outline figures, animals, floral designs, and other decorations carved or etched on hilt and blade. Smiths punched or engraved their own marks, or sometimes Latin inscriptions, on the hilts, pommels, and blades of their creations. In addition, a cross on the pommel indicated that the sword's owner was a member of one of the religious orders of knighthood, such as the Templars or Hospitalers.

Some later swords had graceful and elaborate guards twining around the grips to shield the hand. The tips of the lower guards, or crosses as they were called in the Crusaders' time, were sometimes cleverly carved with the head of an animal or bird or even a human being.

Another kind of decoration, of both blades and hilts, was known as damascening, again because many blades exported from Damascus were embellished with it. This was the art of inlaying gold or silver into an etched steel blade. The design was first carefully engraved deep into the steel, leaving a rough burred edge; then gold or silver wire of the same diameter as the groove was carefully pressed into the groove, and the edges hammered down until the wire held firmly in place. After it was filed smooth, the gold design became part of the blade and remained there even after it had been sharpened many times.

Illustrated are hilts of various types, showing different kinds of guards and pommels, from the earliest Bronze Age swords to the elaborate decorative court swords of the eighteenth century.

Through the ages swordsmiths have adapted their designs to changing conditions, new materials, and new techniques of craftsmanship and warfare. During the Bronze Age, when the brittleness of cast metal

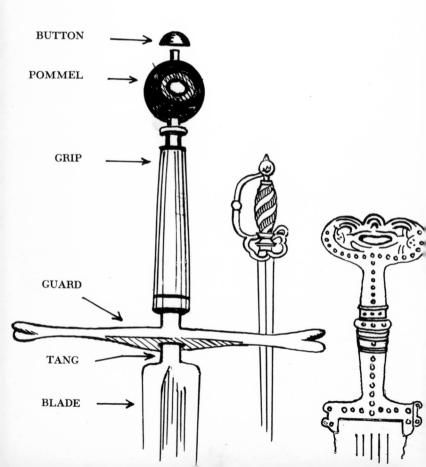

BUTTON

POMMEL

GRIP

GUARD

TANG

BLADE

restricted smiths to short blades, warriors were
equipped with short thrusting swords. But bronze
could not hold a sharp edge for long. With the discovery of iron and of methods of carburizing and,
later, quenching and tempering carbon steel, smiths
were able to build long heavy blades with edges
tough enough to stay sharp. The Celts and other
barbarians, first users of iron weapons in Europe,
fought from horseback or chariots and needed longer
weapons with which to reach their opponents. It was
more natural and certainly more deadly for a mounted
man to slash about him with a cutting weapon, while
his horse was rearing and plunging, than for him to
try to aim a thrust; hence these long swords were
made with two edges and with blunt points. However, when fifteenth-century armorers developed
armor that shielded against slashing blades, swordsmiths had to make cut-and-thrust swords with both
sharp edges and sharp tips. For attempting to cut
through heavy armor, they developed heavy two-

CINQUEDEA

handed slashing swords like the Scottish claymore and the Crusader's long weapon. During the fifteenth century a new type of sword, a cross between the two-handed and the standard blade, appeared. This was the hand-and-a-half or bastard sword, with a grip about seven inches long, which could be wielded with one or two hands.

A strange weapon which came on the scene between 1460 and 1520 in Italy was the cinquedea, so called because its wedge-shaped blade was five fingers wide at the hilt (*cinque* means five in Italian). Some cinquedeas had blades only six inches long and were classed as daggers, while the larger ones that were from fifteen to twenty inches long with blades four inches wide at the hilt were considered swords. The cinquedea was much like the ancient Greek sword and entirely different from any contemporary weapon. No one knows why this anachronistic blade appeared when it did; it may be that a revival of Greek culture in Italy at the time also revived the Greek sword.

As armor became lighter from the fifteenth century on, the rapier became more and more popular because it was lighter and handier than feudal swords. The rapier was flat or triangular in section; slender

54

and made only for thrusting, it frequently had very elaborate guards around the hilt. The court swords, worn by nobles attending the king, were rapiers; the hilts often glittered with gold, silver, and jeweled decorations. In those lawless times, when at any time ruffians might attack a well-dressed traveler along the roads or in the dark alleys which were then city streets, every gentleman wore a rapier as casually as he did his cloak, and usually he carried a dagger as well. From the rapier sprang the épée and the foil, slender, springy, round-bladed weapons used principally for fencing. The rapier was still being carried well into the eighteenth century, especially by mounted men, even after the advent of the horse pistol.

In the seventeenth century the broadsword, a straight heavy blade, was the popular military weapon against an opponent, who still usually wore a metal cuirass; but a hundred years later the cavalry saber, a shorter, slightly curved sword handy for a slashing attack against unarmored enemies, was the standard weapon for mounted troops and was also worn by mounted infantry officers. During the seventeenth century also the cutlass, a shorter, heavier sword than the saber, with a single edge and a sharp

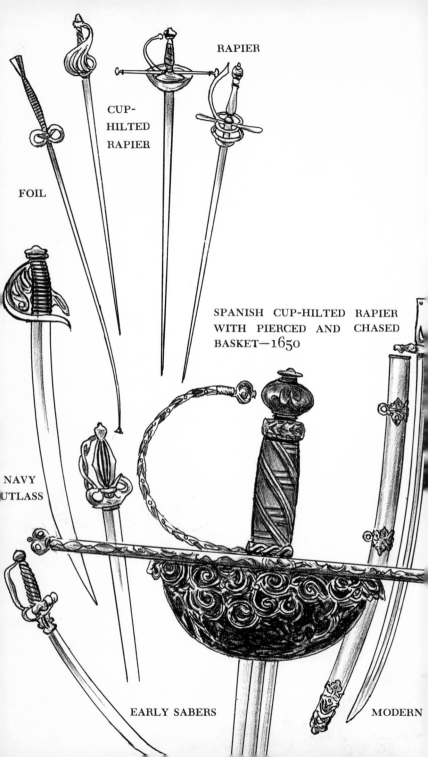

FOIL

CUP-HILTED RAPIER

RAPIER

NAVY CUTLASS

SPANISH CUP-HILTED RAPIER WITH PIERCED AND CHASED BASKET—1650

EARLY SABERS

MODERN

point, was used by seamen when boarding ships or repelling boarders.

Military officers still wore swords as side arms as late as World War I, and they sometimes wear them on full-dress occasions today. During World War II, Japanese officers brought along their swords and sometimes actually led charges with unsheathed blades, but apparently these swords were much more frequently used by their owners to perform ritual suicides.

The Scabbard

The earliest swords were undoubtedly carried in the hand or tied to a cord or strap slung over a warrior's right shoulder. This was not only unhandy but even dangerous: a naked blade bumping against the legs could cause harm. Then, too, the sharp edges of the sword might be nicked against some obstruction.

So it is not surprising that, as early as the Bronze Age, men-at-arms were sheathing their blades in wooden scabbards. These were usually made of two hollowed-out flat strips of wood, bound together with wood or metal bands and tipped with a U-shaped metal chape to protect the end of the scabbard when it struck the ground. The Norse sagas mention wooden scabbards covered with leather and lined with fur. In the first century, scabbards for the broad-bladed sax were made up of many thin flat strips of wood bound together with bronze straps.

Iron Age scabbards were made of two narrow, thin, concave plates of iron forge-welded together. Over the centuries there were periods when scabbards, like swords, were heavily ornamented with gold and silver inlay, decorative metal studs, engraving, and etching. Some were painted in brilliant

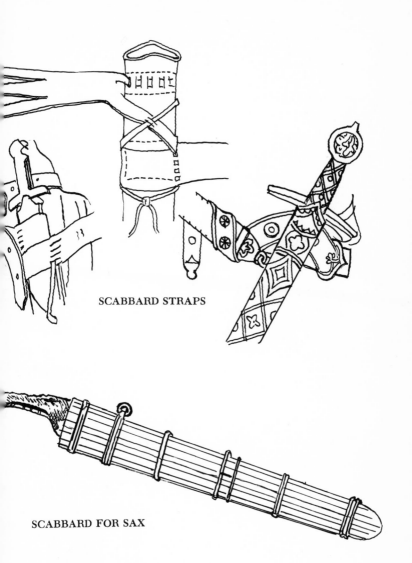

SCABBARD STRAPS

SCABBARD FOR SAX

colors. At other times—during the Crusades, for example—they were made only of unadorned iron and steel and plain leather.

Some swords, like those found in the Danish bog deposits, were tied into their scabbards by means of "peace strings." Apparently it was hoped that men's tempers would cool by the time they untied the knots, but nothing is recorded about the obvious advantage to the man who didn't tie down his sword.

Methods of suspending scabbarded swords varied. Attached to some scabbards were hooks like tiny anchors, which fastened onto rings at the ends of straps slung from a man's belt. Other scabbards were laced to two broad straps, one encircling the waist from the front, the other from the rear, in such a way that the sword hung at the proper angle for withdrawal.

Early scabbards were slung from baldrics, broad straps crossing over the right shoulder with the ends coming together at the left side, just below the waist. Later the baldric gave way to the sword belt, which was worn around the hips and was often richly decorated and embellished. This belt consisted usually of a series of broochlike plaques, square or oblong in shape, each one fastened to the next in line by a

60

gilded decorative hinge. Each plaque had a raised base decorated with a shield, crest, or design in color or gold. This raised boss was secured at each corner by a trefoil, or clover-shaped mount, also gilded or silvered, and the belt was fastened with an ornate buckle. The scabbard was suspended from the belt by straps ending in hooks slipped through rings.

After the early fifteenth century, swords were usually suspended by straps from a separate belt worn diagonally across the hips, while the original "sword belt" was worn for decoration.

The Dagger

6

The dagger is simply a sheath knife used as a weapon and is probably the earliest and most widely used of all weapons, since the knife has always been the most necessary of domestic tools. Even the humblest peasant could afford one; it was easy to conceal, and it could be drawn quickly for attack or defense.

Bronze daggers dating from earlier than 1000 B.C. have been found in Egypt, but as a weapon in Europe the dagger was not widely used before the fourteenth century, where it seems to have developed from the short sax of the Vikings. It was easier to carry and conceal than the sax and was most popular in a variety of forms during the fourteenth and fifteenth centuries, probably because during those two hundred years men wore less and less armor and were, therefore, much more vulnerable to a short blade.

Dagger blades were from six to twenty inches long,

single or double edged, straight or curved. In section they ranged from the needle-slim stiletto to the wide-bladed cinquedea. The cross guards were of many designs, some short and stubby, others swooping in graceful curves around the hilt. Pommels ranged in shape from simple knobs to crescents to the carved heads of people, birds, and animals.

Hilts also ran the gamut. There were perfectly plain iron or wooden grips and elaborately decorated ones embellished with gold and silver inlay, inset jewels, and beautiful carving.

Some daggers had special names and purposes. A type with two projecting disks on the pommel was called an "eared dagger." Another with a slim, almost

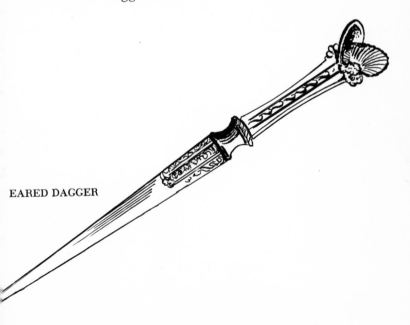

EARED DAGGER

needlelike blade was called curiously "the dagger of mercy." A fallen knight was so thoroughly protected by his full armor that it was almost impossible for the victor to get at him with ordinary weapons for the finishing stroke. This dagger had a blade slender enough to be thrust through the eye slits of a knight's helmet.

In the fourteenth century a two-handed style of fighting became popular. The swordsman held his sword in his right hand as usual but, at the same time, carried in his left a long dagger, called the *main-gauche*, with which he parried his opponent's sword strokes and also made stabbing attacks.

The Bow

7

The bow, the only pre-gunpowder weapon except the sling that could kill at a distance mechanically, dates back to prehistoric times. It was used by Stone Age warriors; the Hittites loosed arrows from their chariots; the Assyrians, the Medes, and the Persians all had archers among their troops. Parthian archers loosed arrows behind them, while their horses seemed to be fleeing; from this technique came our expression "a Parthian shot," meaning a parting shot.

In Europe the Norse knew the bow, as did the Celts, Germans, Greeks, and Romans. The crossbow and the English longbow changed the whole art of warfare in the fourteenth century. The Chinese, the Japanese, and our own pre-Columbian American Indians hunted and made war with bows and arrows. Types of bows varied widely, from the very short bows of aboriginal savages to the great Welsh longbows.

Bows were made of many kinds of wood, of horn,

whalebone, and steel. American Indians preferred the wood of the Osage orange tree, but they also used hickory. The famous Welsh longbow was usually of yew, but basil, ash, and hazel were sometimes used when yew was unavailable.

Early longbows were of two kinds: the self-bow, made from one piece of wood, trimmed and tapered; and the composite or built-up bow. The latter was made of several layers, of which the core was a thin, flat wooden stave. To the stave's belly, the side toward the bowman, was glued a layer of split horn, which always returned to its original shape after being bent by the archer. On the back of the stave, tough, resilient, dried animal sinews were glued lengthwise. This "sandwich" was bound together with wrappings of animal sinew at short intervals and became a much more powerful weapon than the self-bow. The composite bow was usually about four feet long.

The Turks made the best composite bows, capable of extremely long ranges. In a contest in Europe a Turkish bowman shot an arrow 482 yards, but assured his awed competitors that his shot would not be considered far in Constantinople, where the record stood at 838 yards. If this was true, it still stands as the world's record, although modern American bowmen have shot arrows a very respectable 640 yards.

The early bowstring was of twisted hemp, wrapped with a spiral binding of linen cord. It stretched when wet, so the bowman tried his best to keep it dry during a shower to prevent the bow from losing power.

The archer wore a leather cuff on his left wrist, to protect it from the lash of the bowstring. The finger tips of his right hand were protected from the string by small leather finger tabs or by a wooden or metal thumb ring. Early archers grasped the bowstring between the thumb and forefinger of the right hand and drew it back as far as the right breast.

The projectiles fired from the early longbow ranged from feathered arrows, whose wooden shafts were tipped with flint or obsidian chips or iron and steel, to the slender reeds which savage tribes tipped with sharpened fire-hardened wood. The reed arrows were usually loosed from short, weak bows, which provided a short range and almost no killing power. But their heads were tipped with poison, so that even a scratch from the arrow was enough to kill its victim in a few minutes.

Early longbows go back as far as the Neolithic period, in both Asia and Europe. Archers were common in ancient Egypt and Mesopotamia, and thousands of Persian arrows were gathered up from the battlefield of Marathon. For a time during Greek and Roman days the bowman was eclipsed by the phalanx and the legion, but even then the Romans used Cretan archers.

Many fighting men, especially in the Near East and Asia, accustomed as they were to almost living on horseback, learned to shoot the bow while mounted. Their swift squadrons of small but agile horses would swoop down upon the flanks of infantry columns, pour in a flight of arrows, and gallop out of reach in a flash, only to reappear from another direction in a few moments. The European Crusaders met the Saracen mounted archers when they reached the Holy Land and soon learned to respect their skill.

The Crossbow

When knights began wearing hauberks—loose-fitting coats made of thousands of small steel links—the early bowman lost his menace, because his arrows could not penetrate the mail. Then in the twelfth century a new weapon, the crossbow, appeared. It had a wooden stock, much like the later gunstock, to

MAKING CROSSBOW STOCKS

which the bow was mounted crosswise. To bend the bow the crossbowman pulled back the string to a notch in a small cylinder mounted on the stock. To release the string from the notch he simply pulled a trigger. An archer could cock the smaller early cross-bow by placing one foot in a small steel stirrup bolted to the end of the stock and pulling the string back to the notch with both hands. To cock another type, the archer bent over and slipped the bowstring over a hook fastened to a strap hanging from his belt, then straightened up to let the hook pull back the string.

The crossbow could shoot small stones and metal balls as well as arrows. The arrows were much shorter than longbow arrows and were called bolts. They had metal tips, called piles, usually without barbs, of the same diameter as the shaft. Instead of feathers, bolts were fitted with strips of leather or paper.

Bolts from early crossbows were more powerful than the arrows from early longbows, but they were not powerful enough to pierce a "full-proof" hauberk at any distance. Finally armorers began to build crossbows with steel bows, shaped something like the modern leaf springs of an automobile. These new bows had terrific power, enough to send a heavy steel-tipped bolt 475 yards and drive it through steel-

TRIGGER AND REVOLVING COCKING CYLINDER

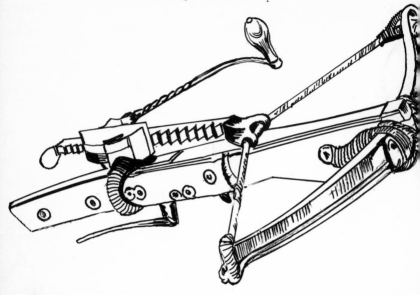

mesh armor at 375 yards. Steel bows were much too stiff to cock by hand; they needed mechanical power, which was relatively slow. There were three types of mechanical actions: the light "goat's-foot"; the ratchet and lever, called the gaffle or cranequin; and the heavy rolling purchase or windlass type, requiring a removable winch with two handles operating a set of cords running over pulleys. This heavy bow was called an arbalest.

The French and Genoese excelled in the use of the

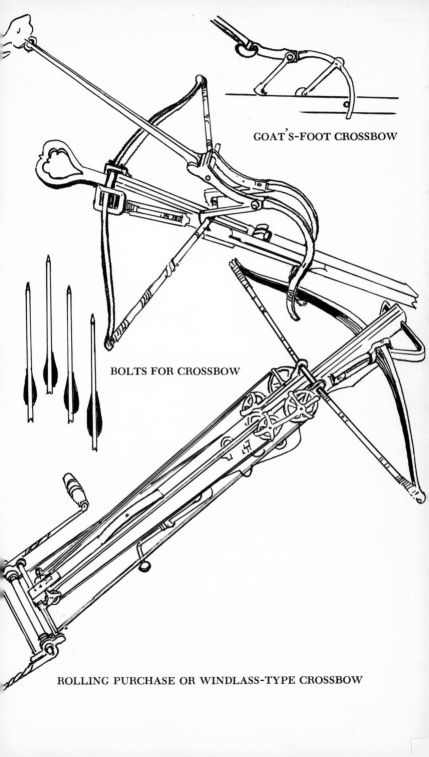

GOAT'S-FOOT CROSSBOW

BOLTS FOR CROSSBOW

ROLLING PURCHASE OR WINDLASS-TYPE CROSSBOW

crossbow. In battle the bowmen were placed in the front line, to bring down as many mounted enemy knights as possible. When the foe's cavalry got too close, the bowmen, in danger of being overrun because of the slowness of their fire, retreated between the ranks of their own cavalry, who were drawn up in formation behind them. From then on the battle became a melee of hand-to-hand conflicts between mounted knights of both sides.

The one serious drawback to the formidable crossbow was its slow rate of fire. Even a good archer could get off only two or three shots a minute. Still those shots were so deadly that armed knights began to demand better armor, and soon armorers found the answer: it was plate armor, thin steel sheets, bent and riveted together. With this protection, which resisted penetration by the crossbow bolt, a knight had a good chance of trampling down a line of arbalesters before they had time to disable his horse. To increase firepower, both the Chinese and Japanese developed repeating crossbows, in which the bolts were stored in a magazine below the stock. However, those bows still had to be cocked for each shot, so that the increase in firepower was not sufficient for repeating bows to be adopted in Europe.

The Longbow

At about the time the knight in plate armor became a serious challenge to the crossbowman, a new weapon appeared on the European battle scene. This was the Welsh longbow, which soon brought about the downfall of the armored, mounted knight. Originally the weapon of the Welsh peasant or villager, the longbow became valued throughout England. Soon, by royal edict, every yeoman in England strove to become proficient with this weapon. These village archers became the backbone of English armies.

The longbowman stood erect, legs spread apart, presenting his left side to the target. He grasped his six-foot-long bow in the middle with his left hand, keeping his left arm fully outstretched. Grasping the arrow and the middle of the string with two fingers, he pulled back the string as far as his right jawbone, sighting along the arrow's shaft. It was this wide stretch that gave the longbow its extra range and power. The archer kept one foot on a sheaf of arrows arranged on the ground; plucking them from a quiver was too slow. On the battlefield he sometimes stood behind a row of sharpened stakes whose butts had been driven into the ground and whose points faced up and out as a protection against charging cavalry.

ENGLISH LONGBOW

He might also be sheltered by a long shield called a mantlet, which was held by a comrade, its bottom resting on the ground, or by a sort of wooden easel propping up a board shield.

A good archer was expected to be able to hit a target 240 yards away with every one of the twelve arrows he had to loose within a minute. The cloth-yard shaft from the longbow had terrific velocity; it

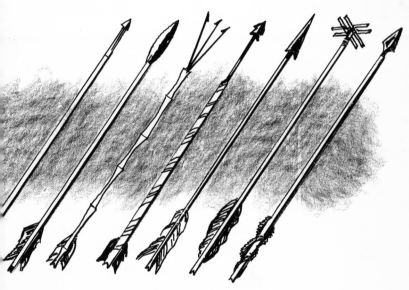

LONGBOW ARROWS. THOSE AT LEFT ARE WAR AR-ROWS. THOSE AT RIGHT ARE FOR KILLING LARGE GAME OR FOR KNOCKING DOWN SMALL ANIMALS AND BIRDS.

could pierce a solid oaken door three and a half inches thick, and was known to have gone clean through the mailed leg of a knight, pierced the saddle and saddlecloth behind it, and penetrated deep into the horse's side.

The shaft of the longbow arrow was called the stole; the notch, which fitted over the bowstring, was the nock; and the head was the pile. The arrow itself measured a cloth yard in length, which was then thirty-seven inches. It was stabilized in flight by three goose half feathers, glued or bound at equal intervals around the shaft at the nock end.

The stoles of war arrows were fitted into the tips by sockets. The tips, which were the same diameter as the shafts, were usually triangular or rounded steel points, without barbs which might affect the accuracy of the flight. Heads with triangular barbed shapes were used mostly for hunting, but occasionally war arrows had barbed piles to make it difficult to pull them out. Arrows with very broad heads were sometimes used in sea battles to tear the enemy's sails and cut his rigging.

A classic example of the power of the English longbow, which has previously been mentioned, was the Battle of Crécy in northern France, August 26,

1346, during the Hundred Years' War. This battle, in which the longbow made its first appearance on the European continent, illustrates the effect the weapon had on medieval tactics.

Edward III of England, at the head of a raiding column, had crossed the Channel and attacked Normandy towns, looting and burning as he went. Informed that Philip VI of France was approaching with a hastily assembled army much larger than his own, Edward retreated toward the coast, hotly pursued by the French. The English were delayed by several river crossings; and as they approached the village of Crécy along a narrow forest track, Philip's forces gained on them rapidly.

When the English emerged from the woods, Edward decided to make a stand at the top of a sloping meadow beyond the trees. He divided his army into three "battles," as divisions were then called: one under his son Edward, the "Black Prince"; the second under two of his dukes; and the third, held in reserve in the rear, under his own command.

These first two battles drew up in line at the top of a small hill, overlooking the thick forest they had just traversed. The knights dismounted and formed in close order in the center of the line of each battle, while their horses were led to the baggage lines in the rear. Flanking the dismounted knights were two battalions of English longbowmen, their lines extending outward from the center like wings.

Groups of peasants were put to work preparing traps for the French cavalry. In front of the lines they scattered spiked obstructions called calthrops and dug trenches that were then camouflaged with brush and grass to make pitfalls.

Then the English sat down to wait. Presently there was movement along the narrow forest track, and soon enemy crossbowmen emerged from the shadows and began deploying across the meadow. Just at this moment the sky darkened and a sudden violent thunder burst over both armies, drenching everyone. It lasted only a few minutes, and the sun soon reappeared.

The French van, made up of a large body of Genoese crossbowmen, advanced upon the English lines and fired a volley of bolts which fell short, possibly because their bowstrings had been wet by the rain. Then the English longbowmen, who had managed to keep their strings dry inside their tunics, opened fire. Clouds of deadly cloth-yardshafts whistled through the air in almost unbelievable numbers, and their greater range found the helpless Genoese with deadly accuracy. The crossbowmen faltered and broke, unable to withstand the hail of arrows, just as the first French knights appeared from the forest. Furious at what they believed to be rank cowardice on the part of their Genoese allies, the French galloped forward and began cutting down their own men.

More French men-at-arms arrived and formed up to charge the English lines, although most of the French army, which greatly outnumbered the English, was still pushing along the narrow forest road. As a result the entire French force was never able to engage at one time. Now the French made their fatal mistake. Instead of directing their attack against the English archers' outflanking wings, they drove straight for the center of the line and the English knights.

As the French knights trotted up the hill, picking their way among the bodies of Genoese bowmen, the English archers poured a hail of arrows into their ranks. Many found their marks in crevices in the knights' armor, but much more devastating was the slaughter of horses. As the French steeds fell, knight after knight was sent crashing to the ground. Utter confusion reigned. The deadly shafts winged down on French reinforcements, until at last their troops were so disorganized that they were easy prey for the knights of the English king, who rode down to dispatch them.

Thousands of French knights, the flower of their chivalry, fell in that battle, as well as more thousands of French foot soldiers and archers. The English losses were almost nil. It was a complete triumph for Edward III. Crécy caused great excitement among military leaders of Europe, and brought about a complete revamping of tactics everywhere; it was also the beginning of the end of the dominance of the armored knight.

8

Polearms:

Spear to Halberd

All weapons with lethal heads fixed to the ends of long poles, such as the spear and the battle-ax, are classified as polearms.

The earliest polearms were the spear and the ax, both evolving from the knife, which some caveman lashed to the end of a stick, hoping to keep out of reach of the claws and fangs of the next saber-toothed tiger he met.

The earliest disciplined troops were spearmen, who remained masters of the battlefield for centuries until they were overthrown by bowmen riding in chariots. Polearms were always the weapons of dismounted warriors and armed peasants, partly because axes and billhooks, needed in farming, were already hanging in the barn when the vassals were called to serve their lord.

The spear was either a light throwing weapon used by both infantry and cavalry, or a heavy thrust-

BEEFEATERS

SWISS GUARDS

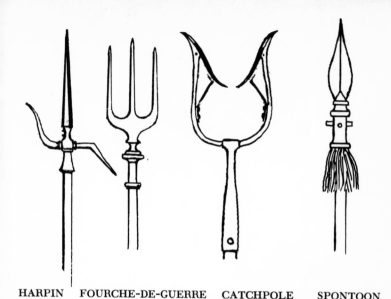

HARPIN   FOURCHE-DE-GUERRE   CATCHPOLE   SPONTOON

ing one such as the Greek hasta, the later Swiss halberd and pike, and the lance of the armored knight.

The spear, of course, could be used only for thrusting, but one day it occurred to some up-and-coming armorer to make a spear more versatile by combining its thrusting power with the chopping stroke of an ax. The result was the battle-ax. A crude form of battle-ax had been used by prehistoric man, who lashed a sharp-edged flint to a stick; the tomahawk of the American Indian was simply a short-hafted battle-ax.

In northern Europe the Norsemen used the war

85

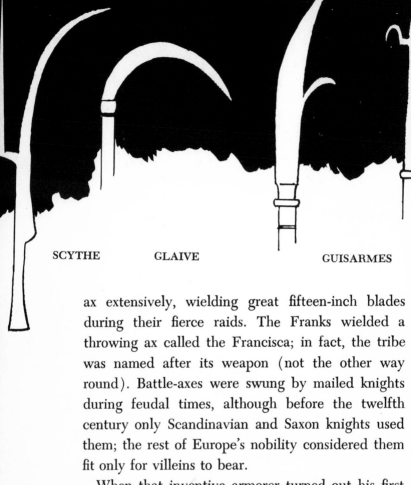

SCYTHE   GLAIVE   GUISARMES

ax extensively, wielding great fifteen-inch blades during their fierce raids. The Franks wielded a throwing ax called the Francisca; in fact, the tribe was named after its weapon (not the other way round). Battle-axes were swung by mailed knights during feudal times, although before the twelfth century only Scandinavian and Saxon knights used them; the rest of Europe's nobility considered them fit only for villeins to bear.

When that inventive armorer turned out his first combination spear and ax he started a long train of

VOULGE   RANSEUR   PARTIZAN   HALBERD

fearsome and ingenious weapons. Almost all of them had sharp thrusting points and some form of cutting blade; beyond that their shapes varied widely. Some included hooks with which to pull a knight from his saddle; others had scythelike blades on one side and sharp teeth on the other. Harpins, or *fourches-de-guerre,* as their name indicates, were shaped like

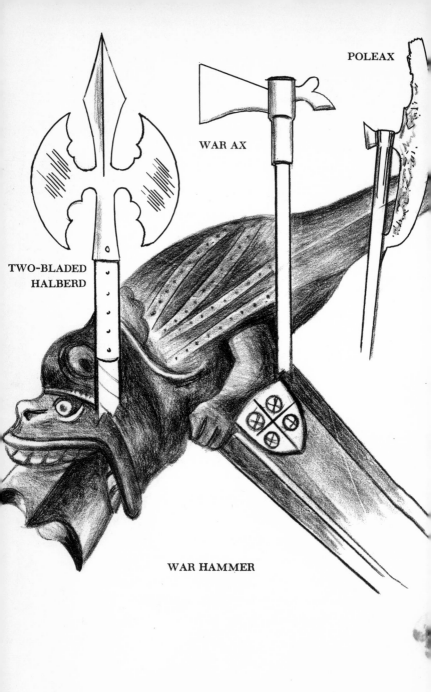

POLEAX

WAR AX

TWO-BLADED
HALBERD

WAR HAMMER

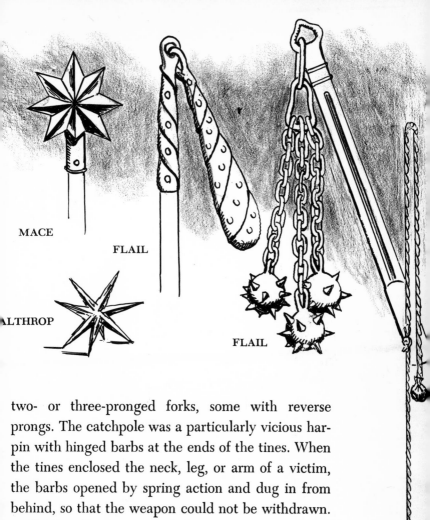

MACE

FLAIL

CALTHROP

FLAIL

SLING

two- or three-pronged forks, some with reverse prongs. The catchpole was a particularly vicious harpin with hinged barbs at the ends of the tines. When the tines enclosed the neck, leg, or arm of a victim, the barbs opened by spring action and dug in from behind, so that the weapon could not be withdrawn.

Illustrated are some of these strange polearms, the war scythe, the glaive, the guisarme, the voulge, the ranseur, the partizan, the war hammer, the *fourche-de-guerre*, the poleax, the catchpole, and the spontoon. Shown also is the famous halberd, invented by the Swiss and still carried by Tower of London Beefeaters and by the Vatican's Swiss Guard.

Related to polearms was another class of weapon developed from the primitive war club. This group included the mace, the flail, and the cudgel. The simplest, the cudgel, was a club with a large knobbed wooden head studded with sharp-pointed spikes. The mace was like a cudgel but had a head of cast bronze or iron, with sharp protruding wings or star points, mounted on a wooden haft. One type of spike cudgel was called the "morning star" because its circle of sharp points resembled rays. Another with a pear-shaped head studded with points was known as the "holy-water sprinkler."

The flail was a development of the mace. From a ring at the end of its shaft, one or more short lengths of chain were suspended, each chain ending in a heavy metal ball studded with sharp points. With the flail a mounted knight could reach far out on either side of his horse and mow down a wide swathe of enemy soldiers.

Another weapon, which shared with the arrow the ability to do damage at a distance, was the sling. It was made of two long strips of braided leather, sinew, or cord, one end of each joined to the sides

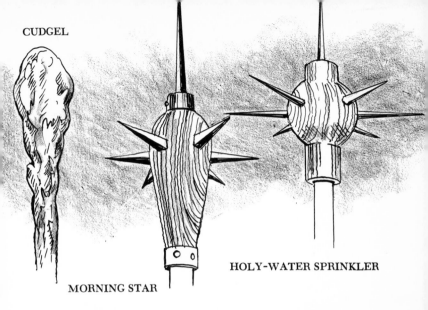

CUDGEL

MORNING STAR

HOLY-WATER SPRINKLER

of a leather patch or pocket which held a stone. The slinger released the stone by swinging his weapon in circles overhead and letting go one end at the proper instant. The Persians and Egyptians included companies of slingers in their armies. The most familiar duel involving the sling is the Biblical encounter between David and Goliath.

In a category by itself on the medieval battlefront was the calthrop. An ancient predecessor of the modern tank obstacle, it was scattered over the ground where enemy cavalry was likely to pass. The calthrop was a kind of iron hedgehog, roughly star-shaped but with points extending in four directions, so that it would lame any steed which stepped on it.

The Feudal Castle

9

We have seen how the insecurity of the so-called Dark Ages resulted in the growth of the feudal system by which kings and dukes took lesser nobles under their protection, while those nobles in turn were liege lords to petty nobles and knights, whose retainers were the peasants farther down the social scale.

Each noble had to have some stronghold where his men could gather during a crisis, where women and children could be safeguarded, and where food, weapons, and equipment could be stored. In medieval times the countryside was dotted with these strong points, which ranged in security from the simple fortified manor house of the poor knight to the frowning, many-turreted, triple-walled castles of king and great nobles.

The medieval architect and engineer engaged in an endless contest during the centuries before gunpowder, the one to design impregnable castles and the other to build siege engines to destroy them.

To understand the problems which confronted the builders of siege machines it is necessary first to examine what the castle builders tried to accomplish. Before the days of heavy artillery the basis of defense of a castle was the stone curtain wall, flanked by numerous towers and protected by a water-filled moat or a steep cliff. This wall had to be breached or scaled before the castle could be captured.

Of course there were other ways of capturing a castle. One was through the treachery of somebody in the garrison, who might be bribed to unlock the postern gate, a small door at the back of the castle. Another was a long siege. Trying to starve out the garrison by siege was a difficult job in medieval days, because the besiegers themselves soon ate up all the food within many miles and found it almost as hard to get supplies as did the besieged. The attacking commander also found it hard to keep his army to-gether for a long campaign. According to medieval law a vassal was required to give only forty days' service at one time to his liege lord. This was so that he would not be kept too long from the tending of his crops, upon which lord and villein depended.

The castle architect used all his cunning to foil any

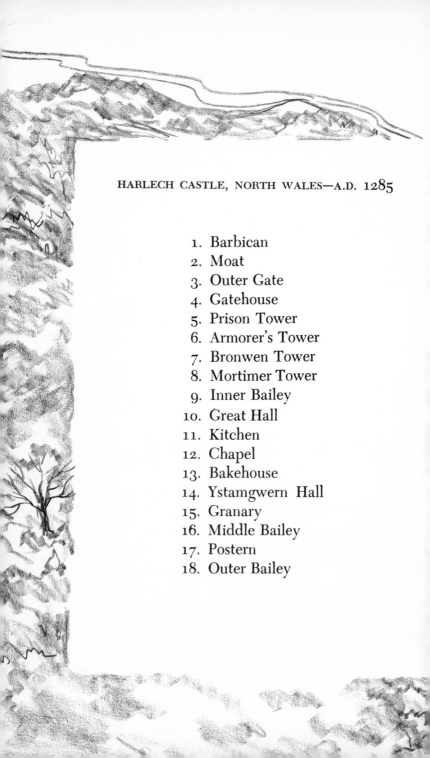

HARLECH CASTLE, NORTH WALES—A.D. 1285

1. Barbican
2. Moat
3. Outer Gate
4. Gatehouse
5. Prison Tower
6. Armorer's Tower
7. Bronwen Tower
8. Mortimer Tower
9. Inner Bailey
10. Great Hall
11. Kitchen
12. Chapel
13. Bakehouse
14. Ystamgwern Hall
15. Granary
16. Middle Bailey
17. Postern
18. Outer Bailey

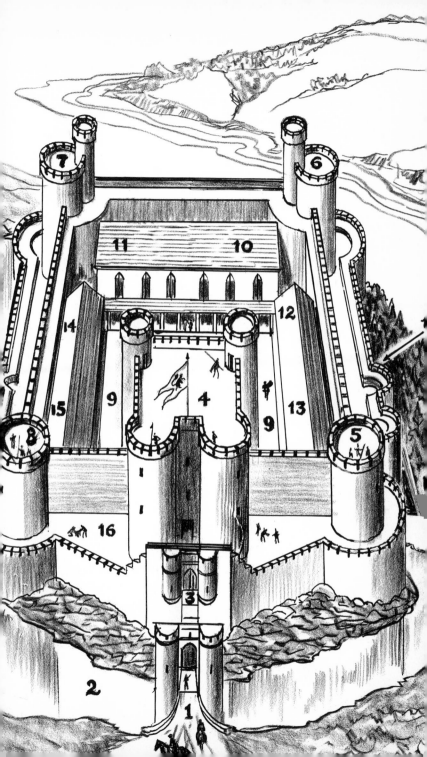

possible attack. To begin with, he tried to find a site offering as many natural advantages as possible, perhaps atop a steep cliff with only one possible approach, or on an island in the middle of a deep river, or on a knoll in a quaking marsh. This is why so many ancient castles were built in bleak, forbidding surroundings. If no natural defenses existed he built them, by diverting a stream into his moat or by digging deep ditches.

In the center of the medieval castle was usually the keep or donjon, the strong tower, sometimes rising two hundred feet in height. Here the lord of the castle and his men-at-arms could make a last stand, in case the walls were breached. Around the keep was an inner courtyard, called the inner bailey, encircled by an inner wall. At intervals along this wall, extending beyond its face, were towers from which archers and spearmen could shoot down upon any foe who managed to reach the base of the walls. In some castles this inner wall was encircled by an inner moat, so that the gate could be reached only by crossing a drawbridge.

Beyond the inner wall lay the outer bailey, encircled by the mighty outer curtain wall, which was sometimes twenty feet thick and thirty feet high. A line of barracks, storerooms, stables, mews for the hunting hawks, workshops for the smiths, armorers, and carpenters, a bakery and brewhouse and many other sheds were built against the outer walls in the outer bailey. They were of wood, often with thatched roofs, so that if the enemy broke in they could all be set afire.

The outer walls, too, had round towers with crenelated tops to protect the garrison fighting on the ramparts. At vulnerable points, roofed wooden balconies, called brattices or hoardings, were built out over the edges of the walls; through slits in their floors the defenders could pour boiling water or oil or molten lead upon the heads of attackers below. At the approach of an enemy the brattices were covered with soaked cowhides, to prevent their being set afire by flaming arrows.

The walls were divided into segments by the round towers and could be sealed off from one another by heavy, iron-bound doors in the towers. Thus, if a section of the wall were scaled by the enemy he could be contained in one section and annihilated. The stairs to the ramparts were located inside the towers and could be closed off to the attackers.

The main gate of the castle was usually its weakest

point and the architect redoubled his efforts toward making it secure. In front of the main gate, across the drawbridge on the outer side of the moat, was a small outer fortification, complete with towers and a gate of its own, called the barbican. The barbican was designed to forestall a surprise attack on the main gate while it was open.

Even if the foe succeeded in storming the barbican, destroying the raised drawbridge, and battering down the massive iron-bound main gate itself, his troubles were far from over. Behind the gate was an arched passage, running under the gate tower, at whose inner end hung a massive iron-barred portcullis, ready to be dropped at the first sign of danger. To add to the misery of any enemies trapped between gate and portcullis, the garrison could pour boiling oil and rain volleys of arrows down upon them through slits in the sides and ceiling of the passage.

The main gate was not the only passage through the walls. Usually one or more gates were located at the rear or sides of the castle. These postern gates were narrow doors, heavily reinforced and guarded, from which the garrison could launch surprise sorties on the enemy or dispatch messengers at night to sneak through the enemy lines to find friends or aid.

The foregoing is a description of a typical twelfth- or thirteenth-century castle, but it must be understood that every castle differed in many respects from every other castle. Topography played a great part in a castle's design, as did the type of attack it might have to withstand. A castle built as a defense against wild tribes along the Scottish border, who had no siege weapons, would be quite different from a central European castle, which might be besieged by well-trained troops equipped with the latest armaments. Then, too, the experience and genius of each castle designer led to variations in the over-all design of a given fortress.

Some castles had single curtain walls, others double and even triple. Some based their final defense on a central keep, others had a number of towers to which the garrison could retire if the walls were breached.

It will be instructive to have a look at an actual castle of the thirteenth century; Harlech Castle, illustrated on pages 94-95, was built in North Wales, in A.D. 1285. It stood above a harbor at the mouth of the river Dwyryd, long since silted up. It is a good example of the concentric-wall castle, fairly new to England at that time but common enough in the East. As far back as 538 B.C. the Persians fortified the city of Agbatana with seven circular walls, one within the next.

Harlech Castle had double walls, with a narrow outer bailey between the outer and inner walls. Attackers who tried to scale the outer walls were under fire both from them and from the higher inner walls, and if they attained the outer bailey they were under even more direct attack from the walls of the inner bailey. Even if the enemy broke into the inner bailey they were still under fire from the four corner towers and the massive gate towers.

10

Siege Machines:

Ballista, Onager, Trebuchet

It would seem an impossible task for an invading force, without firearms or explosives, to overcome the defenses of a strong feudal castle. Yet it was frequently done by assault of one kind or another; the garrison was overwhelmed and the castle razed. How could the storming of a castle be accomplished?

The actual planning and carrying out of such an operation was seldom done by a commander of noble blood. Feudal knights were trained only in hand-to-hand combat, in the use of the sword and lance, and in horsemanship. Most knights were ignorant of even the simplest engineering principles; in fact, most of them couldn't even read or write.

Therefore it was customary for the noble commander of an army bent on reducing an enemy fortress to hire a professional engineer of low birth but high intelligence as a specialist in conducting sieges.

Such men were treated with reluctant respect by the nobles, and they demanded—and received—high pay in gold for their services.

When the invaders appeared before the castle they planned to attack, the siege engineer made a tour of inspection to find any weaknesses and to lay his plans. Formidable indeed appeared a feudal castle battened down against an onslaught. Rising out of a forbiddingly deep, wide, water-filled moat, the sheer stone walls soared high in the air. Every crenelation and tower battlement was crowded with steel-clad archers and spearmen. Columns of smoke behind the brattices indicated that great iron pots of water and oil were aboil on brisk fires. Showers of arrows greeted the slightest move toward the walls.

The first job of the siege engineer was to isolate the garrison, to prevent raiders from sallying forth from within, and to block the entrance of reinforcements or supplies from without. Groups of peasants were put to work, setting up a log palisade around the castle to seal it off and, at the same time, to afford shelter to archers and working parties who would now begin to prepare emplacements for the siege machines.

Finding timber was always a problem, since all the

large trees for miles around would already have been felled, partly for use as building material for the castle and as firewood, and partly to prevent an invader from making use of them.

In medieval days all metal was too precious to use except where it was absolutely indispensable, so the siege engineer had to rely on wood for most of his construction. Often the search for suitable timber was long and wearisome; during their siege of Jerusalem, the Crusaders had to transport all the timber on the backs of camels and Moslem captives from Samaria, fifty miles away.

When at last sufficient timber had been assembled and sawed into beams and planks, construction of the siege engines began. These machines of pre-gun-powder days were of two types, based on the principle of the bow or that of the sling. The lighter ones, which propelled heavy arrows, javelins, or small stones, were usually brought along in the baggage train and assembled on the field; but the larger machines were too massive to be moved far—they had to be built at the site of the siege. They bore such exotic names as catapult, ballista, onager, mangonel, scorpion, and trebuchet. Their purpose was to toss great stones, heavy spears, casks of "Greek fire"

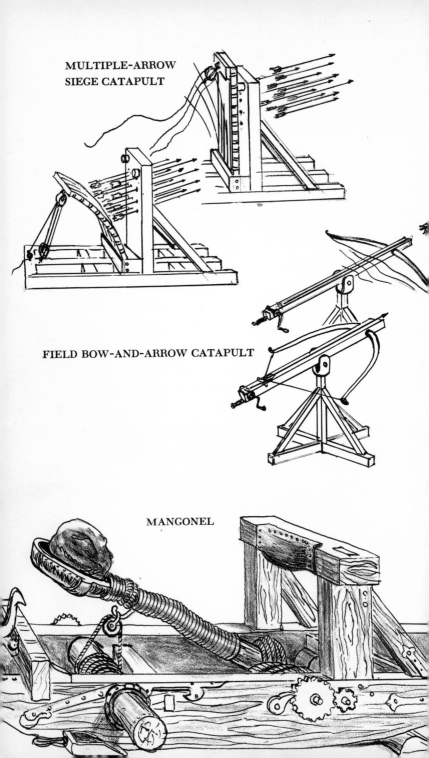

MULTIPLE-ARROW
SIEGE CATAPULT

FIELD BOW-AND-ARROW CATAPULT

MANGONEL

(an inflammable composite of sulphur, lime, and other chemicals), and other missiles against the walls or over them, to damage buildings, start fires, demolish towers, and kill or wound the members of the garrison.

The smaller field, bow-and-arrow catapult was simply an oversized crossbow mounted on a swivel atop a wooden stand. Another type, ancestor of the machine gun, looked like an upright door braced to a base. As many as ten arrows, pointed at the target, were inserted in holes in the "door" with their nocks protruding. A row of springy timbers, whose ends

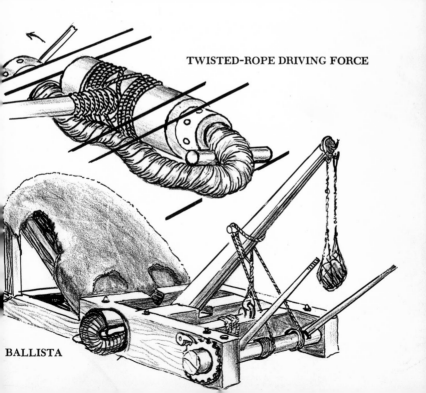

TWISTED-ROPE DRIVING FORCE

BALLISTA

were bolted to the base, was then bent back by a tackle. When the operator pulled the trigger, these timbers sprang forward, struck the nocks of the arrows, and drove them out of the holes and simultaneously into flight. This machine, much like a modern rocket launcher, worked on the principle of saturation fire rather than bull's-eye aiming.

A somewhat heavier machine was the onager, or "wild ass," so named because of the action of its beam, which resembled the kick of that beast. The onager had an oblong base, mounted on wheels, with an upright frame at one end, shaped like an inverted U. Just behind the U a sturdy upright beam was mortised at its lower end to a revolving wooden cylinder whose ends passed horizontally through holes in both sides of the U-frame. At one end of the cylinder was a toothed gear and a ratchet. To the other end was affixed a heavy skein of rope. The rope crossed the frame and was attached to a windlass. To cock the machine, the attackers drew the beam back and down by means of a tackle and twisted the rope in the windlass.

A sling at the upper end of the beam carried a cup in which the missile was placed. When the trigger was released, the rope untwisted and slammed the beam against the padded U-frame, whipping the sling up and forward and sending the missile sailing into the air.

The ballista and the mangonel were both casting engines which had pivoted beams. Some used the twisted rope for power, others a limber tree trunk, which could be bent back in an arc and then released to hurl its missile. Some machines had slings to hold their missiles, others a sort of cup lashed to the end of the beam. The cup type could cast a heavier missile, while the sling had a longer range. A four-ton ballista or mangonel could toss a sixty-pound rock five hundred yards. Some engines had beams fitted with wrappings of rope at their tips, so that they looked like huge boxing gloves. When the beam was released, the "glove" struck the nock of a heavy javelin or arrow laid on the frame and drove it into the air.

The heaviest siege engine, the "Big Bertha" of feudal days, was the trebuchet, or trap gate. It differed from other siege engines in that it did not rely on twisting or bending for power. The trebuchet's beam was pivoted unequally on an axle mounted between two tall A-frames, which were braced by timbers bolted to a base. The beam's longer end was

TREBUCHET

fitted with a sling; suspended from its lower end was a huge, heavily built box, filled with stones or sand. The upper end of the beam was drawn downward by a block and tackle and windlass until it was almost horizontal; when the trigger released the tackle, the enormous weight of the box of sand or stones snapped the beam upright, and the sling whipped its missile into the air.

While the trebuchets and other catapults were being constructed the engineer put men to work building several penthouses. These were long, narrow frames made with roofs, but without floors and ends, set on wheels or rollers so that they could be pushed by the men inside. By pushing the penthouse to the edge of the moat, some of the attackers could fill the moat with stones and pass forward fagots under the shelter of the penthouse roof; when the moat was filled the penthouse could be shoved against the castle wall to undermine it. Here, of course, its roof would be reinforced by bags of sand or earth to ward off heavy stones or pieces of molten lead dropped from the walls.

Under the shelter of the penthouse, a "cat" might be brought forward to demolish the timbers of a gate. The "cat" was a battering-ram made of a huge

109

PENTHOUSE AND "CAT"

section of tree trunk. It was tipped with an iron cap and hung by chains from a sturdy wheeled frame, in which it was swung back and forth. Some penthouses were equipped with towers rising from their roofs. These towers would be filled with archers who would try to force back the garrison from the embrasures above.

If the castle was unusually strong, the engineer might have to build a siege tower. This was a framework which looked very much like a modern, wooden oil derrick, but its front and sides were enclosed with planks and covered by wet hides to prevent it from being set afire. The rear, left open, had ladderlike crosspieces nailed across it, so that men-at-arms could climb up to a roofed, enclosed platform at the top. To the front of the platform was hinged a drawbridge, ready to be dropped on the parapet when the attack began.

A final task was the construction of a large number of scaling ladders to be used when the assault on the castle walls began. After an initial siege of as long as a year, this assault itself might last many days or even weeks.

Now the big siege engines were wheeled or dragged into position along the palisades, and great piles of stones, arrows, and javelins were placed alongside. Archers lined up behind the log palisades and directed a heavy bombardment of stones and arrows against one section of the walls, to cover the penthouses crawling toward the moat below. Stones, fagots, and bags of earth were passed hand to hand from the rear under the penthouse roofs and tossed into the moat, until a slowly rising causeway showed above the surface of the water. When this was firm enough to cross, the penthouses moved slowly forward, and men laid timbers and floored them with planks, amid a futile cascade of rocks, molten lead, and arrows.

A penthouse finally reached the barbican gate and under its protection the "cat" began to smash against the timbers. Meanwhile the siege engineer had begun another operation. From behind a screen of bushes a tunnel had been started, burrowing beneath the moat to one of the large support towers. Relays of diggers labored day and night, timbering the tunnel, hoping the waters of the moat would not drown them like rats. They worked with cloth-wrapped tools because they knew that sentries were posted in the castle cellars to listen for the sounds of tunnel-digging. Each sentry laid his shield flat on the ground and pressed an ear to it. The shield acted as a sort of medieval microphone. If the sentries heard digging noises, a countersap would at once be started to intercept the invaders' tunnel.

Once the attackers gained the base of the tower, undetected, they enlarged the excavation under the foundations, carefully timbering the hole to prevent premature collapse, then piled dry brush and wood around the timbers, and soaked everything with melted tallow. All that was needed now was a spark from flint and steel to start a roaring fire, which would soon burn through the timbering and cause the tower to collapse into the excavation. The attackers meanwhile ran back through the tunnel.

By this time a firm causeway had been built over the moat, on which the tall siege tower could safely roll forward to loom above the parapet. Finally the assault could begin.

At first light, attacking archers began to send thousands of fire-arrows, like tiny comets, arcing over the walls to set fire to thatched roofs inside the bailey. These arrows had, lashed to their shafts, tallow-soaked twists of straw which were lighted just before being loosed. Other archers and crossbowmen aimed clouds of steel-tipped war arrows at the crenelated

113

battlements to keep back bowmen of the garrison. All along the line of the palisades could be heard the creaking of the siege-machines' ropes, the groaning of their bending timbers, and the heavy thumps of beams leaping forward.

The massive siege tower crawled toward the walls, rumbling and swaying on its rollers and steadied by a network of ropes. As it reached the wall, the crash of its descending drawbridge on the parapet was the signal for the general assault. Armored knights leaped across, swinging their great two-handed swords and clearing a section of wall so that the scaling ladders could be set in place. Quickly spearmen in morions (steel skullcaps) and leather jackets swarmed up the rungs, and ranged themselves alongside the knights in desperate combat with the castle's garrison.

Meanwhile the weakened gate, battered by incessant blows of the "cat," finally gave way, and the attackers moved forward to demolish the main gate. When that broke, the knights poured through the passage behind, wrenched off the portcullis with the hastily brought-up "cat," and charged into the outer bailey.

An ominous column of smoke had been pouring

from beneath one of the gate towers for some time; now, with a roar, the tower suddenly disintegrated as the timbering burned through. Swordsmen and archers scrambled over the stones and rubble to take the defenders from the rear. Quickly the outer bailey was subdued and the inner wall so vigorously attacked that the defenders realized their position was hopeless and surrendered. The skill of the siege engineer, plus the valor of the attackers, had triumphed over the stone walls of a medieval castle.

Strange Weapons of Far Lands

11

In ancient times, sophistication in the working of metals was by no means confined to Europe and the Near East. China, Japan, and India, as well as the Arab nations, had skilled craftsmen who understood steelmaking and who could turn out exquisitely wrought and decorated armor and weapons. In fact, Indian craftsmen were the first metalsmiths; by the time of Alexander the Great, Indian sword blades were famous all over the medieval world. Some pieces bore an astonishing resemblance to European arms and armor of their period, although they were separated by half the distance around the earth at a time when communications and transportation hardly existed.

Generally pre-gunpowder weapons were still in use in these and other non-European lands long after they had disappeared in Europe. In the East there were few factories for making weapons and ammunition, and the people were too poor to buy armaments abroad.

Still, they had some very efficient weapons, including a few completely unknown to the European world, such as the Australian boomerang, the Patagonian Indian bola, and the jungle Indians' blowgun.

Richly decorated and bejeweled arms were in use in Persia, India, Turkey, and other Oriental countries for many centuries. Engravers and lapidaries at the courts of the great Moguls of India in the seventeenth century turned out court swords with jade, rubies, and emeralds worked into their hilts in gold and silver settings. They also made daggers with hilts of crystal or of white or green jade, carved in the form of animals' heads and inlaid with jewels or gold. The state scimitar of Murad V (1840–1904), Sultan of Turkey, was encrusted with diamonds, emeralds, and pearls. Although fairly modern in make, it has a blade dating back to 1688 and a scabbard

SCIMITAR AND SCABBARD OF MURAD V

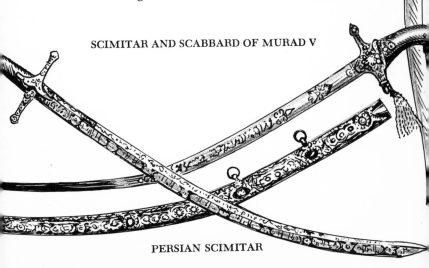

PERSIAN SCIMITAR

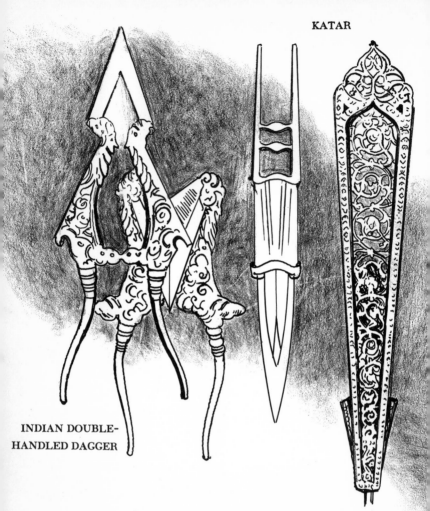

INDIAN DOUBLE-
HANDLED DAGGER

covered with intricately engraved designs and embellished with jewels. People attributed mystical pow-
ers to these jeweled weapons, just as they had in
ancient times. Shown is Murad V's weapon, as
well as a Persian scimitar with inscriptions from the

120

Koran, and a yatagan, or saber, common in Turkey and North Africa.

India was especially rich in strange and beautiful weapons. Illustrated are Indian daggers with triangular, double-edged steel blades and double handles which could be reversed to enfold the blade; also a katar, a knife with two parallel bars as a handle, and another with an openwork, pierced hilt. Also shown is the Indian or Persian shamsheer, from which the scimitar was developed. It has a narrow, thick, curved blade thirty-two inches long and was designed for draw cutting, a stroke by which the blade is dragged along the cut toward the wielder.

In the armory of the former Indian state of Johore, there is a curious sword with a hilt that continues as a gauntlet, almost to the swordsman's elbow, and

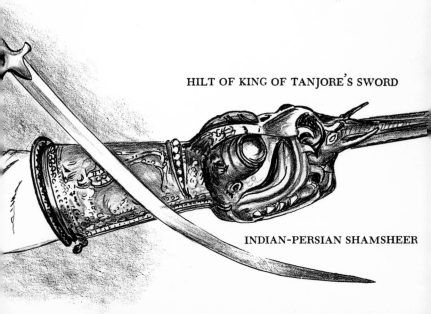

HILT OF KING OF TANJORE'S SWORD

INDIAN-PERSIAN SHAMSHEER

BULLOVA FROM CHOTA NAGPUR

BHUJ-KUTTI

INDIAN SPEARS

is decorated with the figure of a dragon swallowing an elephant. Peacocks, serpents, and dragons were often used as motifs for perforated hilts, reminiscent of the pierced cup-hilts of European rapiers and daggers of the seventeenth century.

Illustrated, too, are several types of Indian axes, such as the bullova, the fighting ax of Chota Nagpur (in India), which has a star-shaped head; several spears, one with a wavy blade, another with curved

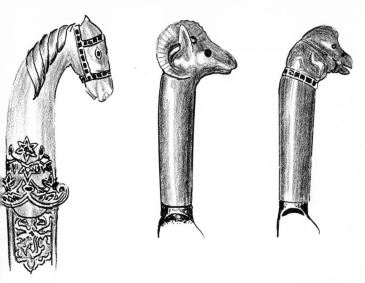

DAGGER HILTS OF ANIMAL HEADS FROM INDIA AND PERSIA

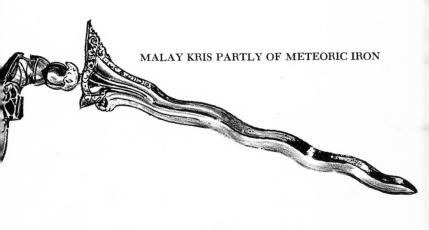

MALAY KRIS PARTLY OF METEORIC IRON

and hooked side cutters; and a curiously shaped knife, decorated with carved elephant heads, called a bhuj-kutti. A particularly vicious weapon was the bagh nakh, or tiger claw. This strange knife had four sharp curved steel claws which left wounds like the claw marks of a tiger or leopard on its victims. The bagh nakh was used by the Thugs, a murderous outlaw sect which flourished in India in the eighteenth century, to identify its victims. A companion weapon

FILIPINO DAGGERS   TALIBONGS

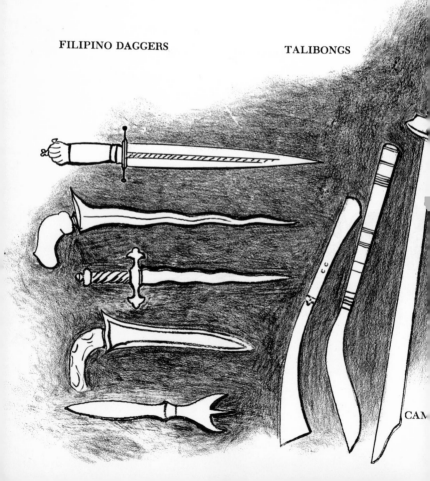

CAM

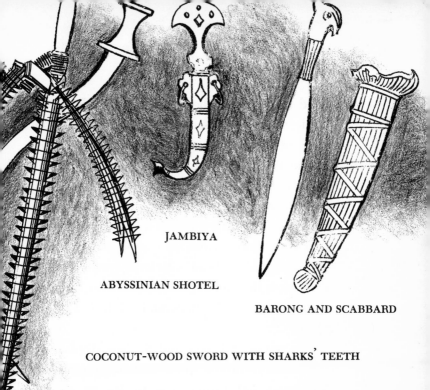

JAMBIYA

ABYSSINIAN SHOTEL

BARONG AND SCABBARD

COCONUT-WOOD SWORD WITH SHARKS' TEETH

was the bich' hwa, a curved knife with steel claws
extending at right angles from the hilt, thus combining the lethal features of the bagh nakh with those of
a dagger.

Page 123 shows three seventeenth-century dagger
hilts from India and Persia. Made of jade and ivory,
they are carved in the shape of a horse's, antelope's,
and camel's head. Also shown is an interesting kris,
or Malay sword, with a hilt in the shape of a bird's

head, representing the Hindu god Garuda. The wavy blade, suggesting a serpent, is made of "iron from the sky," meteoric iron, a metal looked upon as sacred.

The Philippine Islands offer a rich assortment of swords. Filipino smiths knew, from ancient times, how to forge iron and temper steel. Illustrated is the *campilan,* the only two-handed sword used on the islands, with its curious hilt carved in the shape of an animal's or bird's head with wide-open mouth. Even stranger is the talibong, or head cleaver, which has a short, wide, curved blade and a hilt as long as the blade.

The group of knives and daggers displayed here shows the skills of Moro and Tagalog smiths in Mindanao and Luzon. The blades are of several shapes, curved, wavy, and straight, some with guards or crosses like those on European weapons, and others with odd pistol grips. The Moros of Sulu also used a sword with a blade sixteen inches long by three inches wide, called a barong, which was sheathed in a flat wooden scabbard.

Another curious knife is the Arab jambiya, which had such an acutely curved double-edged blade that it couldn't be slipped into an ordinary scabbard; its scabbard had to be made in two pieces which snapped open to allow the blade to be placed inside.

From the Gilbert Islands comes a strange sword called the tebutje. Made of coconut wood, this blade had cutting edges of sharks' teeth fitted into slots. Its long forward-pointing guards were similarly studded with sharks' teeth. Another interesting sword is the shotel, whose origins are Abyssinian; it has a wooden-hilted blade two and a half feet long, shaped like a somewhat straightened sickle.

In old China the soldier ranked far down in the social scale, and the disdain thus accorded him probably included his weapons, which are not remarkable for workmanship. In Japan, on the other hand, the sword was an object of deep veneration; and the best craftsmen devoted much effort to forging the finest blades possible and to decorating them with gold, jewels, jade, and ivory in beautiful designs. Many Japanese swords and scabbards are real works of art.

Japanese sword blades were made of several kinds of steel or of steel and iron welded together. In one method a strip of steel was welded to one of iron, then the combined strip was folded on itself, re-welded and drawn out to its original length. This process was repeated again and again until the metal for the blade was composed of thousands of layers of iron and steel folded one over another, each layer absolutely clean of even the smallest bit of scale that might flaw the blade. Such a blade was the result of many months of labor. While forging it the Japanese smith could produce, by his method of hammering, a pattern in the blade that looked like wood graining. The crucial point in forging a Japanese sword was the formation of the yakiba, the hardened carburized edge which was distinguished by a pearly luster. Since the Japanese sword was always a cutting weapon, the smith had to produce a blade with a very hard edge, which would take and hold a razor-sharpness but was backed up by a softer iron body with some give so that it would not snap off when a heavy blow was delivered.

Swords and daggers are not the only kinds of

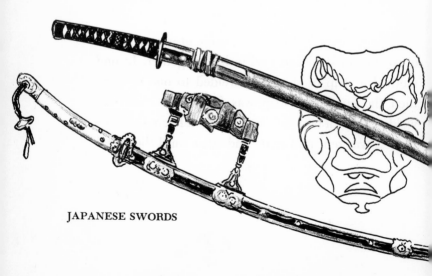

JAPANESE SWORDS

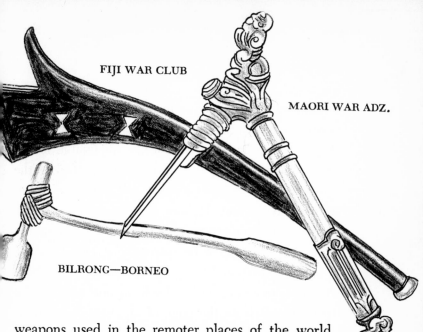

FIJI WAR CLUB

MAORI WAR ADZ.

BILRONG—BORNEO

weapons used in the remoter places of the world, of course. The Fiji Islanders contribute a carved four-foot-long war club with a sharp point on one side. The Maoris of New Zealand were the only people to wield a war adz, which was elaborately carved and decorated; the natives of Borneo carried a bilrong, or war ax, of metal lashed to a wooden handle.

Heading any list of unconventional weapons is the boomerang of the Australian aborigine. This is a rather flat, curved piece of wood, cut from a limb of nearly the right shape. The boomerang has a sharpened inner edge but varies considerably in shape, weight, and degree of curve according to its purpose.

129

A skillful native can perform almost unbelievable maneuvers with this curved wooden "throwing stick." Using a peculiar overhand stroke impossible to describe, he can fling it ahead so that it strikes the ground twice, reverses itself in one grand loop, and returns to his feet. He can also throw it so that it swoops wide and returns to his feet without touching the ground at all; or he can make it circle around a group of trees and bring down a duck *behind* him. A war boomerang with a hook on one end can be made to catch on the edge of an enemy's upraised shield and hop right over it to strike his face. A war boomerang does not return to the thrower.

The boomerang is not an exclusively Australian weapon. The early Egyptians, Assyrians, and some East Indians used steel and ivory throwing sticks; and some African tribes, and even some of our own southwestern Indians had similar weapons. Another unconventional weapon is the bola of the Patagonian Indians. It consists of two round chipped stones fastened to either end of a plaited leather cord. The Indian swings it in circles above his head, aims for his target, and releases it. The rotating bola wraps itself around its victim again and again, leaving him temporarily helpless. Even in modern times, Argen-

LOWGUN

tine cowboys continue to use the bola to entangle the legs of cattle that they wish to "cut out."

The blowgun of the South American Indians and other primitives is also in a class by itself. It is usually a hollow reed, often more than six feet long, into which a small feathered razor-sharp bamboo dart is fitted. The end of the pipe is held in the mouth and aimed at its quarry, then a puff of air from the lips of the tribesman sends it on its way. Although the blowgun's range and penetration are not great, its dart is coated with curare or some other poison so that the slightest puncture will kill a victim quickly.

Another odd weapon is the fighting armlet of the Ouled Nail, a North African tribe. This is a metal band, from one side of which protrude sharp spikes. Slipped over the arm it becomes a vicious weapon in hand-to-hand fighting.

Finally mention must be made of the iron war fan of the Japanese samurai. This was used in conjunction with the sword, much as the *main-gauche* (left-hand dagger) was used in Europe to parry thrusts of the rapier. Edgewise its iron blades could deal a lethal blow.

Shields, Helmets, and Armor

12

While the shield is not strictly a weapon, it was always so much a part of offensive and defensive combat, particularly together with the sword and the lance, that it must be included in a description of weapons before gunpowder.

Certainly any Stone Age tribesman must instinctively have reached for the nearest chunk of firewood, or wrapped a fur around his arm, to ward off the flint ax of his enemy from the next valley. We know that warriors before 1000 B.C. carried round flat shields of bronze. They were about two feet wide, finished with circular ridges around a central boss and fitted with a handhold riveted to the back. To strengthen the bronze face, layers of wet hides impregnated with boiling wax were laid in behind the frame; when the leather dried it made a strong, rigid backing.

Early Mycenaean shields were shaped like figure

SHIELDMAKER LINING BRONZE SHIELD WITH CUIR-
BOUILLI (LEATHER BOILED IN WAX)

eights and were large enough to reach from a man's neck to his calves; the Hittites, who fought from chariots, used shorter shields shaped like double-bitted axes.

Later on, shields were made with wicker or wooden frames covered with layers of tough bullhide or solid wooden panels. They were decorated with bosses, portraits, or designs in bright colors and in gold.

The classic Greek shield, round or oval, was deeply hollowed and had leather loops to slip over the left arm. Greek vases show warriors in battle carrying their shields in what at first appears to be a very awkward position: horizontally before them at shoulder height. Yet this was the only practical way; if the soldier had held his shield upright in front of him, his knees would have struck its bottom and much of his vision would have been blocked.

The Roman legionary carried a squared-off shield of semicylindrical shape, reaching from chin to knee. The curved shape gave additional protection to the foot soldier's body. Roman cavalry, however, carried small round shields.

The Vikings treated their shields with great veneration; to lose one in battle was almost as great a disgrace as to lose one's sword. Their shields were so large that they slept under them at night in the fields when out on raids, and young warriors were admonished to come home with their shields or on them. Vikings gave their shields such poetic names as "Son of the Sea Kings" or "The Spear's Path."

By the end of the tenth century, when mailed mounted men-at-arms became rulers of the battlefield, the great Norman kite-shaped shield was the favorite. Its wedge shape, narrowing toward the bottom, gave the mounted knight protection on his left side from the shoulder to well below the knee. This shield remained popular in the north of Europe well into the second half of the twelfth century, but in the south a straight top became the fashion.

In contrast to the huge shields of the eleventh and twelfth centuries was the small round shield called the buckler, popular in Scotland for parrying blows. Sometimes it was called the "fist buckler" because it was small and light enough to be carried by a metal handle held in the left fist, left arm straight, instead of being held by loops over the left forearm. Another fairly small round shield, rather like the buckler, was called a target.

By the thirteenth century, shields became shorter

136

and wider and were curved like the legionaries' shields of a thousand years before. The shield's shorter length now enabled a soldier to sling it over his back and free his left hand for the reins. The adjustable strap by which it was slung was called the guige. Below the guige were three straps in horizontal lines, called enarmes; the knight thrust his forearm through two of them and grasped the third in his hand. He

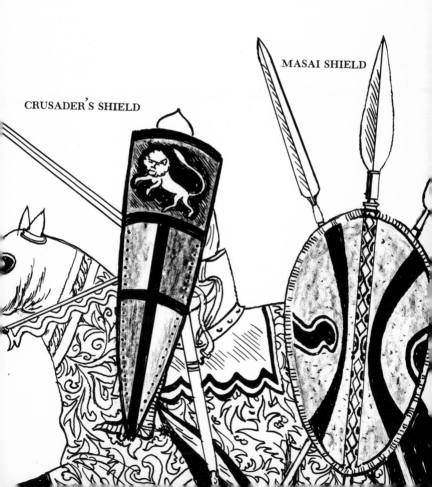

MASAI SHIELD

CRUSADER'S SHIELD

could release the third to grip the reins, since the two over his forearm still held the shield in place.

The shield was still being used in the sixteenth century by certain troops long after the harquebus, or early firelock musket, had appeared; and even as late as World War I portable machine-gun shields were used. Many primitive tribesmen throughout the world, like the Masai in East Africa, still carry their tribal shields, but now mostly as decorations.

Armor, of course, is not literally a weapon; yet, like the shield, it has played such an important part in warfare—often bearing the responsibility for changes in weapon design, not to say the very tactics of battle —that it must also be included in this book. Because the helmet was the earliest form of armor it will be described first.

The Helmet

The helmet came into being immediately after the sword and spear. To protect the head during combat was instinctive; as far back as the eighth century B.C., Assyrian warriors wore tall, conical bronze helmets. The cone seems to have been the most nearly perfect shape for defense, because it deflected blows from any direction.

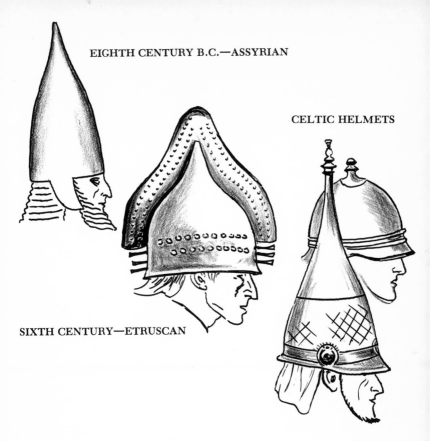

EIGHTH CENTURY B.C.—ASSYRIAN

CELTIC HELMETS

SIXTH CENTURY—ETRUSCAN

HEAUMES WITH RIVETED PLATES

Illustrated is a conical Etruscan helmet of bronze, dating from the sixth century B.C. Its metal crest ends at the bottom, fore and aft, in three short metal rods. A double row of bronze rivets runs around this helmet, just above the rim, as well as along the edge of the crest.

Illustrated also are two Celtic bronze helmets: one, a very tall conical shape with a small visor; the other looking very much like the German patent-leather *Pickelhaube* of early World War I, but without its spiked tip. Also shown is a Gaulish round helmet with a crest, from which a pair of horns extend; and a Dacian helmet made of metal bands forming a cone, the spaces in between filled with bronze plate.

The Greeks used helmets of various types, probably derived from Cretan and Mycenaean models. Some were reminiscent of the modern pith helmet; others were made with long cheek guards that extended well below the chin on either side, and with nasals that came down to cover the nose like old-style football nose guards.

Paintings on Greek vases often depict Greek warriors in combat stark-naked—except for the helmet; and the Romans reported a tribe who stripped naked before going into battle but who also wore helmets.

GREEK HELMETS

GAULISH AND DACIAN HELMETS

KETTLE-HATS

Helmets changed little until the twelfth century; then a new shape, called the kettle-hat, became popular. It had a low rounded crown and a very wide brim, all in all quite different from the conical model. Perhaps it gave better protection to neck and shoulders from a glancing blow from above; at any rate for a time it was widely worn.

Up to the beginning of the thirteenth century almost all helmets were some form of skullcap. To protect his neck and chin the knight wore a hood of mail—part of the hauberk or mailed shirt—which covered his head except for a small aperture in front for eyes and nose. Now came a new conception. This was the great helm that covered the entire head, top, front, and back, leaving only narrow slits in the front to look through. It was almost the size of, and looked much like, an old-fashioned coal scuttle. The early helm was supported entirely on the top of the head, so that it turned with the head, but was buckled to the mailed shirt with straps to help steady it.

Naturally the top of the head needed a lot of padding to support such a weight, as well as to deaden blows. Knights usually wore their hair long and bunched atop the skull, under a light padded cap called an arming cap. Over this went the hood of mail, and sometimes over this a padded cloth ring, on which the great helm rested. Despite the padding the helm was so heavy that it caused great strain on the neck; hence, eventually it was built to rest on the shoulders.

Although it certainly gave almost complete protection to the face, the great helm was so clumsy that it was finally abandoned for warfare and was employed only for tilting at tournaments, where some effort was made to avoid serious injury. The great jousting helms looked even larger than they were because of the knights' custom of topping them with towering crests in the form of fanciful birds' or beasts' heads, stars, dragons, antlers, or even small banners fluttering from tiny staffs. An enamored knight might add to his crest the glove or stocking of his ladylove.

Early in the fourteenth century, a new type of helmet called the basinet was invented for combat. It probably sprang from the light metal arming cap which, when the great helm was abandoned, was for a time the only protection for the head. The basinet was deeper and heavier than the arming cap. All around its lower rim hung a curtain of fine-mesh mail protecting the neck, the shoulders, and the mouth and chin. This made the hood of mail unnecessary.

GREAT HELMS WITH CRESTS—AT THE LISTS

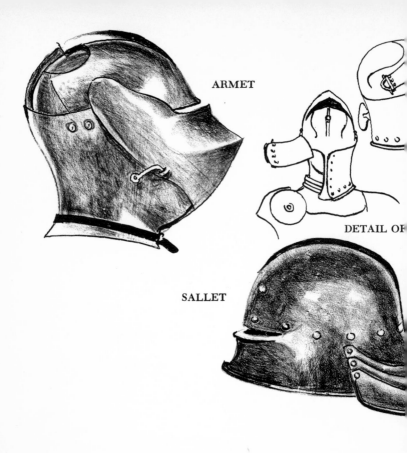

ARMET

DETAIL OF

SALLET

To fill the gap in front between the brim of the helmet and the mail curtain, the basinet was fitted with a hinged visor shaped like a pointed snout, which covered the face completely when lowered but could be pushed up over the forehead to afford better vision. The visor had eye slits and tiny holes for ventilation.

146

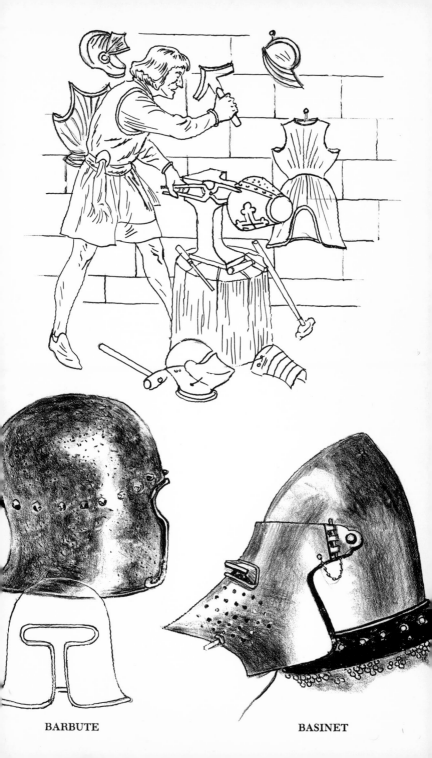

BARBUTE

BASINET

In the fifteenth century, armorers improved on the snout-shaped basinet with several neater, closer-fitting helmets. One was the armet, built on the principle of the hinged cheek plate. The plates, one on either side, could be raised to don the helmet and permitted a much closer-fitting base and a smaller, stronger visor. In battle, when the cheek plates were lowered, they locked together, forming, with the lowered visor, a complete guard of steel. By the time the armet was designed, knights were wearing plate armor, hence it could be bolted to the rigid collar of the cuirass, eliminating altogether the need for mesh armor.

Another new type of helmet was the sallet, of German origin, a development of the earlier kettle-hat. It came down very low in back; in fact, some had such long tails that they had to be articulated to allow them to bend when the wearer wanted to look upward. The front of the sallet, in some models, came down almost to the chin, making an eye slit necessary, and was held in place by a chin strap. Under the sallet the bunched-up hair of the wearer was held in place by a padded arming cap, just as in the days of the great helm. A bevor, a small piece of armor curved to rest on the upper chest and to cover neck and chin, was often worn with the sallet.

FIFTEENTH-CENTURY TURKISH HELMET

CHINESE HELMET

JAPANESE HELMET

At about the same time, the Italians produced the barbute, a rounded casque without brim or visor, which came down to the shoulders, enclosing the face in front except for a T-shaped opening. The crossing of the T formed the eye slit, while the vertical slit below it permitted air to reach nose and mouth.

Illustrated, too, are some examples of Turkish, Chinese, Indian, and Japanese helmets to show the skill of artisans outside Europe.

JAPANESE HELMET

TURKISH HELMET

INDIAN HELMET

Body Armor

It is impossible to say just how far back the wearing of armor can be traced. Before metal came into use, warriors wore heavily padded cloth or leather garments, sometimes toughening the leather by boiling it in wax. When men learned to make sheet bronze, they fashioned bronze scales like oversized fish scales, punched holes in them, and sewed them in overlapping rows to the outsides of garments.

The Mycenaeans, Greeks, and Romans hammered out breastplates, backplates and greaves (shin guards) of bronze for their soldiers. Greaves were important because the shins were unprotected by shields. The Greek hoplite and Roman legionary also wore a sleeveless leather jacket called a cuirass (*cuir* in French means leather) which was secured by a sort of metal belt, consisting of two bands hinged at the back and buckled together in front. This belt was held in place by additional bands of metal, which passed over each shoulder and were riveted front and back to the crossbands.

The legionary, also, wore a helmet copied from the Greeks, of leather strengthened by metal bands, and carried a small round or oval shield.

For centuries only the head, upper body, and shins

BARBARIAN   ROMAN LEGIONARY

were protected by armor; then about the first century a new kind of flexible armor was invented. It was to change warfare completely and bring the mailed knight to the center of the battle scene. This was the metal fabric popularly called chain mail, although a more accurate name would be mesh or link mail. Composed of thousands of tiny, interlinked steel rings, it was somewhat similar to the modern flexible fireguard, although the linkage was different, as can be seen in the illustrations of different types of mail.

The mesh mail was made into a loose tunic which slipped over the head and hung down below the knees, split so that the wearer could sit a saddle. The tunic had long sleeves, sometimes long enough to cover the hands, and a hood which covered the head like the cowl of a monk's habit. This garment was at various times called a byrnie, a haubert, and finally a hauberk. Later, leggings of mail, called *chausses,* which were held up by straps from a belt, were added; and still later a garment called the habergeon, a shorter version of the hauberk.

Now for the first time in history a mounted, helmeted man-at-arms was fully protected against the crude weapons of the foot soldier; the hauberk marked the beginning of a centuries-long reign of the mailed knight on the battlefield.

Only a man of wealth or property could afford a hauberk. About 250,000 hand-forged and hand-tempered steel rings went into this knightly garment; each ring had to be linked by hand to each of the rings around it. It took a very skillful armorer a long hard day to fasten together 250 rings, or three years to complete the entire garment, at a cost of about $12,000 in today's money.

The average, poor foot soldier was lucky to acquire a casque, a plain conical steel cap, or at most a steel breastplate. From the first century B.C., when Gaulish blacksmiths began to hammer the little links together

155

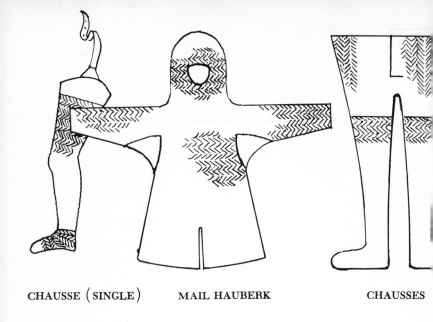

CHAUSSE (SINGLE)   MAIL HAUBERK   CHAUSSES

to make coats of mail, until the fourteenth century, armor changed very little in principle, although after about the eleventh century there were small improvements. For instance, instead of making helmets out of several sections riveted together, armorers now made them all in one piece. The poleyn, a kneecap of iron plate, appeared in the thirteenth century. It was strapped on over padded breeches, called "gamboised cuisses," which were pulled on over mailed greaves or demigreaves (strips of mail covering the front of the leg only, and laced together behind). Evidently the *chausses* alone had not proved enough protection for the kneecap and thigh against a vig-

156

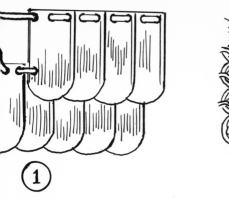

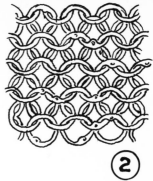

1. SCALE ARMOR. INDIVIDUAL SCALES SEWN TO
   LEATHER OR FABRIC SHIRT OR COAT.
2. CHAIN OR MESH MAIL. EACH RING LINKED TO THE
   FOUR AROUND IT BY RIVETING.
3. IRON RINGS SEWN CLOSE TOGETHER ON LEATHER
   JACKET.
4. DETAIL OF MAIL COVERING SHOULDER AND ARM-
   PIT. CONE-SHAPED PIECE OF PLATE STRAPPED
   OVER ELBOW.
5. STRAPS AT BACK OF SOLLERET OR MAILED SHOE.

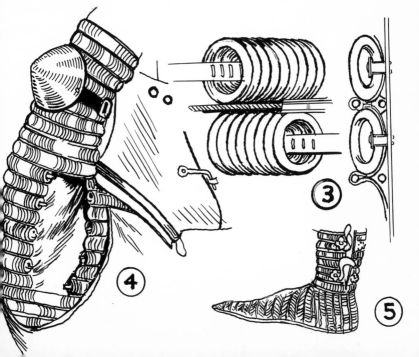

orous sword slash. Some hauberks were tailored with double or triple thicknesses of mail over vital places.

By the thirteenth century men-at-arms began to wear garments of leather or quilted fabric, reinforced with rows of small steel plates sewn across them. These garments were worn over the hauberk and beneath the surcoat, a loose, rather short-skirted coat which some authorities believe the Crusaders originated to keep the sun from heating metal armor to unbearable temperatures. However, the surcoat was also extensively worn in the cool climate of Europe, perhaps to keep armor from rusting in the rain or to display the coat of arms of the wearer. After 1350 a tuniclike garment called the jupon replaced the surcoat, but by the fifteenth century it had been discarded and the knight rode again with armor uncovered. It was sometimes painted black but was usually "alwyte," as shining, polished armor was known.

Up to the first quarter of the fourteenth century, men-at-arms were still wearing substantially the same kind of armor used by the Gaulish barbarians during the first century; but within fifty years, by about A.D. 1350, almost all knights were sheathed in armor made of steel plates which covered them from head to toe.

SQUIRE'S SURCOAT—1350

KNIGHT WITH TUNIC LACED DOWN
FRONT. SWORD AND DAGGER WITH
CHAIN FASTENING—1350

This sudden change in the style of armor was due to no mere whim of fashion, but rather to a desperate struggle for survival. For a thousand years the mailed knight had been able to dominate the field; but within a short period after 1320 the steel crossbow, the English longbow, and the Swiss halberd had become so deadly that the knight had to have better protection to survive.

The first suits of the new armor were a combination of plate and mail. The cuirass, or breast- and back-plate, consisted of sheets of thin, tough steel cut and bent to fit the body; but arms and legs were still covered with mail, although the joints were now reinforced: at the elbows by small plates called couters, at the knees by poleyns, and at the shoulders by espaulieres, or spaudlers as they were known in England.

As armorers became still more skillful they shaped tubes, called rerebraces and vambraces, to cover upper and lower arms, and cuisses to shield the thighs. Presently they learned to construct articulated pieces to cover places where movement was necessary, such as shoulders, elbows, knees, and ankles. Narrow steel plates were so connected that one plate slipped over the next by means of knobs sliding in slots at either end. This permitted considerable movement.

160

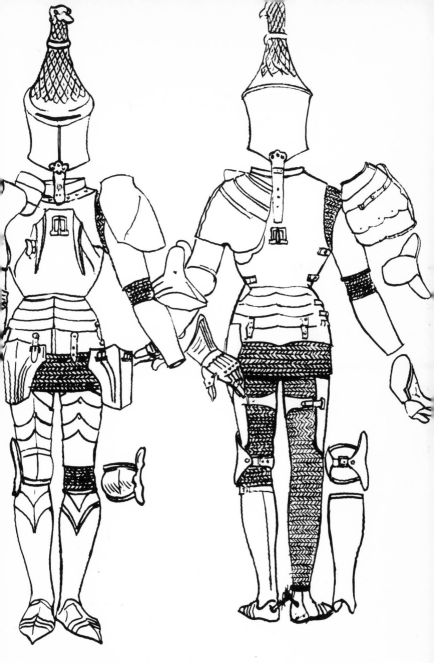

FRONT AND BACK VIEW OF PLATE ARMOR, SHOWING
METHOD OF FASTENING

The final flowering of the armorer's craft was the full suit of plate armor, comprising the cuirass covering the front and back of the torso and often flaring over the hips, cuisses to shield the thighs, poleyns and couters for the knees and elbows, and greaves for the shins. The feet were protected by articulated steel shoes called sollerets. For a time, fashion decreed that sollerets should have such exaggeratedly long pointed toes that a knight was unable to walk if unhorsed, but of course no knight ever admitted that he could be unhorsed. When a knight did have to fight afoot, he had to ask somebody to chop off a few inches from the tips of his sollerets.

When the visor of his helmet was lowered, the armored knight was literally encased in steel, except for where he sat in the saddle, and so he was relatively safe against arrows and the thrusts of polearms. Unfortunately his horse was not, since it was impossible to armor a horse so completely that a cloth-yard shaft wouldn't find a vulnerable spot.

The weight of a suit of armor varied considerably, depending upon the size of the knight and the completeness of the suit. Each armorer had his own ideas of the number, design, and weight of the pieces required for complete protection. The cost also played a part, since the lighter the weight of an adequate suit

of armor the more it cost. However, even the lightest
suit was heavy enough to require the services of one
or two squires, apprentice knights, to put a knight
into it; and he needed a particularly massive horse
called a destrier, built like a truck horse, to carry
him—after he mounted from ladder or mounting
block. Early illustrations show knights being lowered
into the saddle from above by block and tackle, but
these may be examples of medieval humor.

The Battle of Crécy, in 1346, proved that the armored knight could not stand up to the new military
tactics; the cannon and harquebus, which appeared
shortly afterward, completed his downfall. This hap-
pened just in time, for the latest suits of armor were
so beautifully built and so lavishly decorated that
only the richest nobles could afford them. Eventually soldiers went back to lighter armor, usually wearing only helmets and cuirasses; certain mounted
troops continued to do so long after firearms came
into common use.

Armor in the East

Contemporary with the armorers of Europe were
the skilled craftsmen of Turkey, India, Japan, and
China, who were artists and decorators and jewelers

165

JAPANESE ARMOR OF LEATHER,
LACQUER, AND SILK— 1700

CHINESE ARMOR OF EMBROIDERED SATIN, WITH O'
LAPPING PLATES RIVETED INSIDE—SEVENTEE.
CENTURY

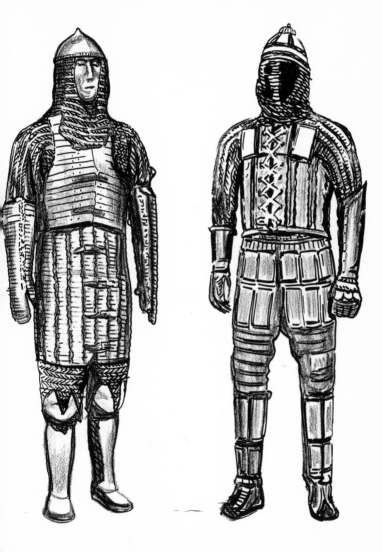

EIGHTEENTH-CENTURY (SIND) INDIAN SUIT OF STEEL,
BRASS PLATES, AND SCALES CONNECTED BY LINKS

as well as metalsmiths. The Crusaders soon discovered, after crossing the Bosporus, the excellence of Turkish armor. Mail coats were worn all through the Near East, plate armor almost never. Eastern armor was only about half the weight of European; partly because the Moslems were smaller than the Crusaders and rode lighter horses, and partly because of the much warmer climate, they relied on fleetness and agility instead of on massive power.

Still their mail coats were strengthened by strips of plate riveted to the mail at important points. The Turkish mail coats of the fifteenth century, which were very much like those worn by the Seljuk Turks during the Crusades, were reinforced by riveted steel bands. Illustrated is a fifteenth-century Turkish suit of steel plates and links articulated by internal straps. Also shown is a suit of embroidered satin with overlapping steel plates riveted inside. Worn in the seventeenth century by an officer of the Imperial Chinese Palace Guard, during Emperor Shuh Chih's reign, its helmet is decorated with a curious crest tipped with two feathers.

Japanese splint armor of the sixteenth century is made up of alternating scales of iron and hard leather, joined together with leather thongs. This type of armor called *hiodoshi*, or "flame color," could be worn only by members of five great noble Japanese families.

An eighteenth-century Sind (Indian) suit made of steel and brass plates and scales, connected by links, completes the illustrations. These are but a tiny sampling of Eastern armor, which remained in use somewhat longer than armor did in Europe—although gunpowder originated in China, it was not applied in the East to firearms until long after cannon and muskets were common in Europe.

A Dictionary of Ancient Weapons

ADZ: see WAR ADZ.

AILETTE: a square guard of metal plate, worn on the shoulder over MAIL during the thirteenth and fourteenth centuries.

ANKUS: an Indian elephant goad with a spike and hook on the end.

ARBALEST: a powerful medieval CROSSBOW whose bow of steel was cocked by a two-handled winch.

ARBRIER: the wooden stock of the CROSSBOW.

ARCHER'S RING: a wooden or metal ring worn on the right thumb to protect it from the bowstring.

ARMET: a late-medieval closed helmet, made of hinged parts, that fitted the head, chin, and neck.

ARMING DOUBLET: a padded garment, reinforced by mail, worn under medieval armor.

ARMING GIRDLE: a sword belt, usually ornate, backed with mail and worn around the hips.

ARMING POINTS: laces to fasten parts of metal armor together.

ARMLET: a metal arm band with spikes, used in North Africa.

ARMOR: Protective battle clothing, usually made of cloth, leather, or metal.

ARROW: the missile shot from a bow. It usually had a straight wooden shaft and a head of stone or metal.

ASSEGAI: a wooden spear, usually with an iron tip, used by South African tribes.

BAGH NAKH: an Indian weapon with four or five curved steel claws.

BALDRIC: a broad strap worn over the right shoulder, with ends joining at the left side to support a sword.

BALLISTA: a medieval siege engine used to hurl heavy missiles.

170

BARBICAN: the small fortification of a medieval castle, on the outer side of the moat. It had towers and a gate.

BARBUTE: an Italian shoulder-length helmet of the fifteenth century. It enclosed the face, except for a T-shaped opening.

BARDS: pieces of armor for a horse's neck, chest, and flanks.

BARONG: a swordlike weapon, with a thick back and thin edge, used by the Philippine Moros.

BASINET: a light, fourteenth-century, steel helmet with a visor. Around its lower rim hung a short curtain of MAIL. See also CAMAIL.

BASKET HILT: a sword hilt with a basketlike metal covering to protect the hand.

BASTARD SWORD (also called hand-and-a-half sword): its GRIP was about seven inches long and it could be wielded with one or both hands. Fifteenth century.

BATTERING-RAM: a huge beam with an iron head, sometimes slung from a frame by chains, used to beat against a wall or gate to demolish it.

BATTLE-AX: like our woodcutting tool. Prehistoric axheads were made of flint, later heads of metal.

BATTLEMENT: the notched parapet topping a castle wall.

BEC-DE-CORBIN: a fifteenth-century war hammer with a long point like a crow's beak.

BEVOR: a piece of armor worn around the neck to protect throat and chin.

BHUJ-KUTTI: a short Indian single-edged knife with a long handle.

BICH' HWA: a curved Indian knife with steel claws extending at right angles from the hilt.

BILLHOOK: a polearm with a hooked blade used in farming and war.

BILRONG: a metal battle-ax used in Borneo.

BLOWGUN; BLOWPIPE: a long hollow reed or tube through which darts are propelled by force of the breath. Used in

Borneo and by Indians of South America and the West Indies.

BODKIN: a small dagger.

BOLA: a cord, with a weight at each end, used to hurl at and entangle victims. Patagonian Indian.

BOLO: a Philippine knife or sword.

BOLT: a short, metal-tipped arrow, usually without barbs, shot from the CROSSBOW.

BOOMERANG: a flat, curved throwing stick, with a sharp inner edge, that returns to the thrower. Used mainly by Australian aborigines. See also WAR BOOMERANG.

BOSS: an ornament, often in the center of a shield or on a bridle.

BOW: a strip of wood, bone, or metal bent by drawing back the bowstring and released to propel an arrow.

BRASSARD: plate armor for the entire arm.

BREASTPLATE: a piece of armor covering the body from the neck to below the waist.

BRICHETTES: armor protecting the hips and thighs.

BRIGANDINE: plate armor riveted to a canvas garment and covered with silk. Late Middle Ages.

BROAD ARROW: arrow with a broad, barbed head.

BROADSWORD: a seventeenth-century sword with a straight, wide, single-edged blade used for cutting.

BUCKLER: in the Middle Ages, a small, round shield held at arm's length and used to parry blows rather than cover the body.

BULLOVA: an Indian battle-ax often with a star-shaped head.

BYRNIE: tenth-century Danish body armor. See also HAUBERK.

CALTHROPS: iron weapons with four spikes, scattered on the ground to lame horses.

CAMAIL: chain mail, usually hung from BASINET, to guard the neck.

CAMPILAN: the only two-handed Philippine sword.

CASQUE: an open helmet.

CAT: an iron-tipped battering-ram hung from a PENTHOUSE.

CATAPULT: a medieval siege engine resembling a large CROSS-BOW, mounted on a swivel and stand.

CATCHPOLE: a polearm with a fork whose tines had spring blades to prevent disengaging the weapon.

CHAPE: the metal tip at the bottom of a sword scabbard.

CHARIOT: a wheeled cart used in battle.

CHAUSSE: mail leggings held up by straps attached to a belt.

CHEEKS: pieces attached to the sides of a helmet to protect the ears and cheeks.

CINQUEDEA: an Italian sword or dagger with a blade five fingers wide at the hilt. 1460–1520.

CLAYMORE: a Scottish two-handed sword of the fifteenth and sixteenth centuries.

CLOTH-YARD ARROW: an arrow 37 inches long.

COMPOSITE BOW: a bow made of several layers.

CLUB: a heavy wooden stick often studded with spikes.

COUTER: the elbow piece in a suit of armor.

CRANEQUIN: a medium-sized CROSSBOW with a rack and pinion used to draw back the bowstring.

CREST: the ornament surmounting a helmet.

CROSSBOW: a medieval weapon that discharged BOLTS, stones, and other missiles. Its bow was mounted crosswise on a stock.

CUDGEL: a short, heavy club.

CUIRASS: a breastplate and backpiece, originally made of leather, coupled to make a sleeveless jacket. First worn by Greeks and Romans.

CUIR-BOUILLI: leather boiled in oil or wax, beaten and molded to shape, and allowed to harden.

CUISSE: armor to protect the thigh.

CURARE: poison extracted from a South American vine and smeared on BLOWGUN darts.

CUTLASS: a heavy, single-bladed short sword used in navies.

173

DAGGER: a sheath knife used for stabbing. The European dagger, developed from the SAX, was most popular in the fourteenth and fifteenth centuries.

DAGGER OF MERCY: see MISERICORDE.

DAMASK SWORD: a sword made in Syria, Persia, and India. The blades were etched to reveal the beautiful watery pattern of the iron crystals.

DESTRIER: a knight's heavy war horse.

DIRK: a dagger used by Scottish Highlanders.

DOKYU: a Japanese repeating CROSSBOW.

DONJON: a strong fortified tower, the heart of a castle's defense.

EARED DAGGER: a fifteenth-century dagger with disks standing out like ears on the pommel.

ELBOW COP: elbow guard of plate armor.

ÉPÉE: developed from the RAPIER, a light sword with a sharp-pointed blade but no cutting edge. Used in dueling and fencing.

ESPAULIER: the shoulder piece in a suit of armor.

FALCHION: a medieval curved sword with a broad blade.

FLAIL: a heavy metal ball, studded with sharp points, hung from a chain attached to a handle.

FLAMBERGE: a long sword with wavy edges.

FLETCHER: an arrow maker.

FOIL: a fencing sword with a light, springy blade, tipped with a button. Derived from the RAPIER.

FOURCHE-DE-GUERRE: see HARPIN.

FRANCISCA: a Frankish battle-ax, often used for throwing.

GAMBESON: a quilted shirt worn under armor.

GAUNTLET: an armored glove.

GLAIVE: a large-bladed polearm resembling a HALBERD.

GOAT'S-FOOT BOW: a CROSSBOW cocked by cam action.

GORGET: a curved plate of armor worn around the neck to protect the throat.

174

GREAVES: armor to protect the shins.

GREEK FIRE: used in sieges, one of several incendiary mixtures containing sulphur, lime, and fuel.

GRIP: the part of a sword grasped by the hand.

GUISARME: a POLEARM of the eleventh to fifteenth centuries.

HABERGEON: an eleventh-century coat of mail, shorter than the HAUBERK.

HALBERD: a POLEARM combining a spear point and ax blades.

HAND-AND-A-HALF SWORD: see BASTARD SWORD.

HANGER: a light SABER of the seventeenth and eighteenth centuries.

HARNESS: a name applied to armor in the Middle Ages.

HARPIN: a POLEARM with a two- or three-pronged fork.

HASTA: a heavy Greek spear used for thrusting.

HAUBERK; HAUBERT: a loose-fitting coat of chain mail. Eleventh to thirteenth centuries.

HEAUME: a heavy thirteenth-century helmet worn over a hood of MAIL or a steel cap.

HELMET: an armored head covering.

HIODOSHI: Japanese armor made of alternating scales of iron and leather. From the sixteenth century.

HOLY-WATER SPRINKLER: a shafted war club studded with spikes.

HOPLITE: a heavily armed Greek infantry soldier.

JACK: a padded coat, sometimes interlined with mail plates, worn by the rank and file in the fifteenth and sixteenth centuries.

JAMBIYA: an acutely curved Arab knife.

JAVELIN: a light spear for throwing or thrusting.

JUPON: a tuniclike successor to the SURCOAT. Fourteenth and fifteenth centuries.

KATAR: an Indian knife with two parallel bars connected by crosspieces to form the handle.

KEEP: see DONJON.

KRIS: a Malayan sword often with a wavy blade made of meteoric iron.

LAMES: metal strips that overlapped to form articulated armor for the shoulder, SOLLERETS, and GAUNTLETS.

LANCE: the horseman's spear.

LATCH: a sixteenth-century English name for the CROSSBOW.

LEGIONARY: a Roman foot soldier or cavalryman belonging to the main army.

LOCKET: the band around the scabbard with a ring for attaching straps.

LONGBOW: a powerful wooden bow, usually about six feet long, drawn by hand. It originated in Wales.

MACE: a clublike weapon with a metal head from which protruded sharp starlike points.

MAIL: armor made of interlocking steel rings.

MAIN-GAUCHE: a dagger for the left hand.

MANGONEL: similar to the BALLISTA.

MANTLET: a large shield whose base rested on the ground.

MILITARY FORK: see HARPIN.

MISERICORDE: a dagger with a needlelike blade that could be thrust through the eye slits of a helmet.

MORION: a visorless steel helmet worn by foot soldiers. Spanish origin.

MORNING STAR: a CUDGEL set with spikes resembling rays.

NOCK: the notch in the end of an arrow.

NUT: a catch to hold back the string of a CROSSBOW.

ONAGER: a medieval siege machine that hurled stones as from a sling.

PARANG: see BARONG.

PARTIZAN: a broad-bladed POLEARM.

PENTHOUSE: a movable gallery with a strong roof that permitted besiegers to approach the castle walls under cover.

PIKE: a spearhead attached to a long wooden staff, used by foot soldiers.

PILE: the metal tip of a BOLT.

PILUM: a Roman spear.

PLATE ARMOR: armor made of solid steel plates.

POLEARM: a cutting or thrusting weapon mounted on a long staff.

POLEAX: a POLEARM with an ax blade on one side and a hammer or spike on the other.

POLEYN: an iron-plate kneecap strapped on over padded breeches. Thirteenth century.

POMMEL: the knob at the top of a sword hilt.

PONIARD: a small dagger with a triangular or square blade.

PRICK SPUR: a spur with a single point instead of a ROWEL.

QUARREL: a square-headed BOLT.

QUARTERSTAFF: a long stick wielded with one hand at the middle and the other between the middle and either quarter point.

QUILLON: one of the two arms that make the cross guard of a sword.

QUIVER: an arrow case.

RANSEUR: a type of POLEARM.

RAPIER: a light, slender, two-edged sword used only for thrusting. Popular from the fifteenth to the eighteenth centuries.

RINGED ARMOR: armor made by fastening rows of metal rings to a cloth or leather backing.

RONCIN: a war horse, lighter than the DESTRIER.

ROWEL: a toothed wheel attached to most modern spurs.

SABER: a curved single-edged cavalry sword.

SALLET: a fifteenth-century helmet of German origin that projected over the back of the neck.

SAX: a short broad-bladed dagger.

SCABBARD: a sword or dagger sheath.

SCALE ARMOR: armor made by fastening scales of horn, leather, or metal to a backing of cloth or leather.

SCALING LADDER: a light ladder used in scaling walls.

SCHIAVONA: a sixteenth-century Venetian BROADSWORD.

SCIMITAR: a curved SABER with the cutting edge on the outside. Used chiefly by Arabs and Persians.

SCORPION: a medieval siege engine used to hurl stones. Similar to the ONAGER.

SCUTUM: a curved oblong shield covered with leather. Carried by Roman legionaries.

SCYTHE: a POLEARM used for farming and war.

SELF-BOW: a bow made of a single piece of wood. See also COMPOSITE BOW.

SHAMSHEER: a curved Indian or Persian SABER.

SHOTEL: an Abyssinian curved sword.

SLING: a pouch, containing a missile, attached to two long straps. The missile is released by swinging the sling and loosing one strap.

SOLLERET: an articulated plate-armored shoe.

SPANDREL: a Roman shoulder guard.

SPAUDLER: the English name for ESPAULIER.

SPEAR: a long-shafted thrusting or throwing weapon.

SPEAR THROWER: a strap or stick used to give greater range to the spear.

SPONTOON: a half PIKE.

SPUR: a sharp instrument, attached to the heel of the horseman, used to urge on the horse. See also PRICK SPUR, ROWEL.

STILETTO: a small slender-bladed DAGGER.

SURCOAT: a knight's military robe of the thirteenth and fourteenth centuries.

SWORD: a long-bladed knife with a hilt, used for cutting and thrusting.

TALIBONG: a Philippine sword with a heavy curved blade and often a very long hilt.

TALWAR: an Indian saber.

TARGET: a small round shield, popular in the eleventh and twelfth centuries. Similar to the BUCKLER.

TEBUTJE: a sword made of coconut wood with cutting edges of sharks' teeth fitted into slots, used in the Gilbert Islands.

TORTOISE: see PENTHOUSE.

TREBUCHET: the largest of the medieval siege engines. When a weight attached to the shorter arm of a lever fell, the longer arm hurled a heavy missile with great force.

VAMBRACE: a metal tube for protecting the forearm.

VISOR: a hinged frontal piece on a helmet to protect the face.

VOULGE: a POLEARM with a spear point projecting from an ax-like head.

WAR ADZ: an ornate Maori weapon like our carpenter's tool.

WAR BOOMERANG: It is heavier than the ordinary BOOMERANG and does not return. When a hook on one end catches onto the edge of the enemy's shield, the weapon will strike him in the face.

WAR FAN: a Samurai fanlike weapon with iron blades. The left hand used the fan in parry and attack, while the right hand wielded a sword.

WAR HAMMER: a weapon combining ax blade, spear, and hammer.

WHISTLING ARROW: an arrow with a large hollow head pierced with several holes, which whistles when in flight.

YATAGAN: a curved saber used in Turkey and North Africa.

Index

181

182

twisted-rope driving force, 105, 106-107

Urban II, Pope, 9

vambraces, 160, 179
Vikings, *see* Norsemen
visors, 146, 148, 179
voulge, 87, 89, 179

Wales:
    Harlech Castle of, 94-95, 99-100
    longbow of, 12-13, 65, 66, 75
war:
    and armor, 138

and the bow, 65, 75, 78-82, 160
and firearms, 15, 38, 165
war adz, 129, 179
war ax, *see* battle-ax
war boomerang, 130, 179
war club, *see* club
war fan, 132, 179
war hammer, 35, 88, 89, 179
war scythe, 86, 89, 178
weapons:
    definitions of, 170-180
    development of, 1-15
    excavation of, 36-38
whistling arrow, 179
windlass-type crossbow, 72, 73

yatagan, 119, 121, 179